Welcome

A Training Course of the National Safety Council

The National Safety Council is America's leading nonprofit safety advocate – and has been for over 100 years. As a mission-based organization, we focus on eliminating the leading causes of preventable death so people can live their fullest lives. We focus our efforts where we can make the greatest impact: workplace, roadway and impairment.

NSC starts at work – where people put everyday strategies in place to solve problems. We give companies resources workers can actually use around risks they are actually facing, or will be. We create a culture of safety to not only make people safer at work but also because it has the potential to make people safer beyond the workplace. Research shows safer workplaces save money and increase productivity, but more importantly, they create a mindset that values safety.

NSC has a long history of convening with its unparalleled network of safety leaders to make people's lives safer on and off the job. We tap the expertise, talent and passion of our network to develop research and ready-to-use toolkits to help companies tackle important issues affecting their workers. Every one of our employees, member organizations and strategic partners have one thing in common: a commitment to enable people to live their fullest lives.

NSC uses research and data to drive better, smarter, more personal safety programs. From perception surveys and assessments to tracking the trends, we use our insight to create real, usable, experiential education, training and tools to mitigate risk. We also engage government across national and local levels to advocate for awareness and drive polices that create a culture of safety.

Save lives, from the workplace to anyplace.™

NSC First Aid, CPR & AED

Table of Contents

Acting in an Emergency

Objectives

- State how your actions can make a difference to a victim of injury or sudden illness.
- List the goals of helping a victim in an emergency.
- Identify how to contact Emergency Medical Services (EMS).
- List ways to be prepared in case of an emergency.
- Describe when consent is needed for helping a victim.
- List the 6 steps to take in all emergencies.
- Describe when to (CALL 9-1-1) and what information to give.

Video Review

What are your 4 goals when you help a victim?

1. _____

   _____

2. Scene _____

   _____

3. Check life threat conditions _____

   _____

4. call 911 _____

   _____

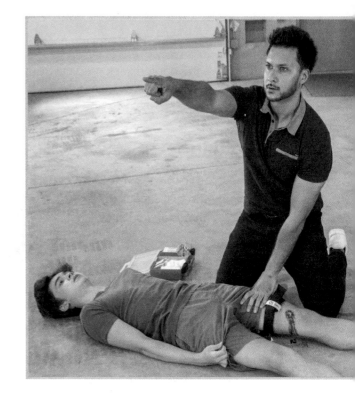

Notes:

Circle **True** or **False** for each of the following statements:

Check the victim quickly before calling 9-1-1.   True   False

Ask a responsive adult for consent for you to give care.   True   False

Do not move a victim unnecessarily.   True   False

Follow the same 6 steps in any emergency. **Write in the missing steps:**

1. Recognize the emergency.

2. _Safe scene_

3. _Life threating conditions_

4. (CALL 9-1-1) or the local emergency number.

5. Obtain consent and provide care.

6. Have the person seek medical attention when needed.

Calling 9-1-1

When you (CALL 9-1-1), the responding dispatcher will ask you questions such as:

- Your name
- The phone number you are using
- The location and number of victims
- The victim's approximate age, sex and condition
  For example: Is the person responsive? Breathing? Bleeding?
- What happened to the victim and any special circumstances
- What is being done for the victim

The dispatcher may also give you instructions on how to help the victim. Stay on the line until the dispatcher says you can hang up.

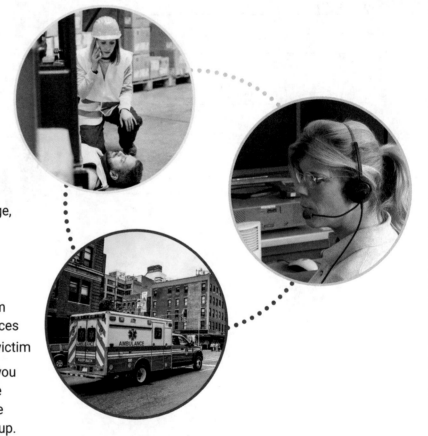

Emergency Response Plans and Good Samaritan Laws

_____

_____

_____

_____

Components of a First Aid Kit

A well-stocked first aid kit should be present in your home, vehicle and workplace. Ensure the first aid kit is in a locked container kept out of reach of children. The contents of the kit should be checked regularly, and all items should be replaced as they are used.

Recommended contents of a first aid kit include:

- Adhesive Bandages
- Adhesive Tape
- Antibiotic Application
- Antiseptic
- Burn Dressings
- Burn Ointment
- Cold Pack 4 x 5 in.
- CPR Breathing Barrier

- Eye Covering
- Eye/Skin Wash
- First Aid Guide
- Foil Blanket
- Hand Sanitizer
- Medical Exam Gloves
- Roller Bandages
- Scissors

- Splint
- Sterile pad
- Tourniquet
- Trauma pad
- Triangular Bandage

https://L.ead.me/FA-Kits

Scan the following QR code or go to the website listed to see the most recent recommendations for what should be included in a first aid kit.

Scene Safety Activity

What kinds of hazards should keep you from entering the scene of an emergency and risking your own safety?

_____

_____

_____

_____

Module Summary: Acting in an Emergency

- O Your primary goal is to ensure the victim gets help quickly.
- O (CALL 9-1-1) or your local emergency number for all emergencies.
- O Give victims **only** the care you have been trained to give.
- O **Always** check the scene for safety and **then** the victim before beginning to provide care.

6 Steps to Follow in Emergencies

1. Recognize the emergency.
2. Check the scene for safety.
3. Check the person.
4. (CALL 9-1-1) or the local emergency number if necessary.
5. Obtain consent and provide care.
6. Have the person seek medical attention when needed.

Notes:

Preventing Disease Transmission

Objectives

- List standard precautions you can take to prevent the transmission of disease.
- Identify personal protective equipment (PPE) to protect yourself from infection.
- Demonstrate how to remove medical exam gloves.

Video Review

If you do not take precautions, what kinds of diseases could be spread during first aid?

_____

_____

_____

_____

Avoid contact with body fluids such as:

_____

_____

_____

_____

What precautions can you take to prevent exposure to a victim's body fluids?
Check all that apply.

☐ Use personal protective equipment, such as medical exam gloves.

☐ If you do not have medical exam gloves, put your hands in plastic bags or have the victim dress the wound.

☐ Wash your hands with soap and water before and after giving first aid.

☐ Do not touch your mouth, nose or eyes when giving first aid (do not eat, drink or smoke).

☐ Use an alcohol-based hand gel if soap and water are not available.

☐ If you are exposed to blood or another body fluid, wash immediately with soap and water and then call your health care provider. At work, report the situation to your supervisor.

Glove Removal

Learn the Skill

Put on a pair of medical exam gloves. Practice removing them without touching the outer surface of the gloves with your bare skin, because the glove surface may be contaminated after providing first aid.

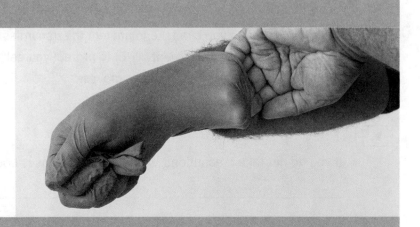

Performance Checklist

Skill Steps

☐ **1.** Hold your hands away from your body, with fingers pointing down.

☐ **2.** With 1 hand, grasp your other glove at the wrist or palm and pull it away from your hand. **Then** pull the glove the rest of the way off.

☐ **3.** Holding the removed glove balled up in the palm of your gloved hand, insert 2 fingers under the cuff of the remaining glove.

☐ **4.** Remove the glove by stretching it up and away from the hand and turning it inside out as you pull it off.

☐ **5.** Dispose of the gloves safely and wash your hands.

☐ **Complete Skill**

Module Summary: Preventing Disease Transmission

FIRST AID STEPS

1. Avoid contact with all body fluids.

2. Use gloves and other barrier devices.

3. Follow precautions to prevent exposure to pathogens, which cause disease.

4. Decontaminate all surfaces as soon as possible with a commercial body fluid disposal kit. Or clean with detergent, rinse with water, and then sanitize with a 10% bleach/water solution. Leave the bleach solution on the spill for at least 2 minutes before wiping it.

Additional Resources: On the OSHA website, **osha.gov**, search for Bloodborne Pathogens Standard 1910.1030.

Check the Victim

Objectives

- Describe how to perform the initial assessment of a victim.
- Demonstrate how to check the victim for life-threatening problems.
- List the victim's history information to obtain.
- Describe how to perform a physical examination.

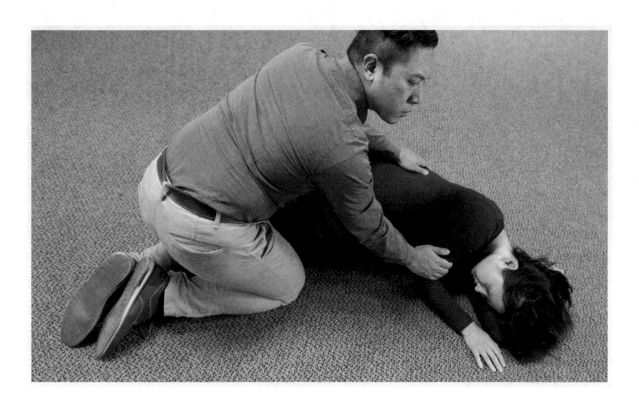

 ## Video Review

Circle **True** or **False** for each of the following statements:

After determining the scene is safe, the first thing you should do when you approach a victim is check for responsiveness.	True	False
If the victim occasionally seems to gasp, this means the victim is breathing normally.	True	False
Do not stop to (CALL 9-1-1) until you've checked the victim all over and have bandaged any bleeding wounds.	True	False
Check a responsive breathing victim immediately for bleeding that may be life-threatening.	True	False
If you find a person who is not breathing normally, conduct a full physical examination to look for possible causes.	True	False

Initial Assessment

Learn the Skill

Pair up with another classmate to practice the initial assessment of an unresponsive victim.

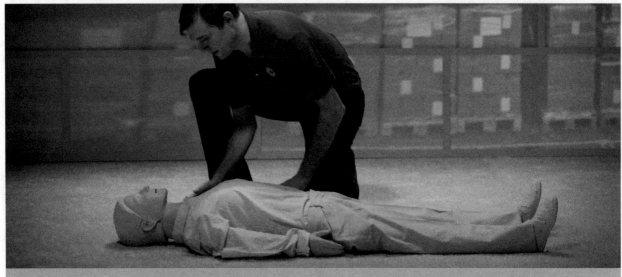

Performance Checklist

Skill Steps

☐   **1.**   Ensure scene safety.

☐   **2.**   Check the victim for responsiveness.

For a responsive victim:

☐   **3.**   Ask the victim what happened and about their condition.

☐   **4.**   Have someone (CALL 9-1-1). If alone, correct any life-threatening conditions you see first (such as severe bleeding) before calling 9-1-1 and continuing to check the victim and providing other care.

For an unresponsive victim:

☐   **3.**   Call for help:

    a.   Shout for someone to (CALL 9-1-1) and get an AED. Keep the phone at the victim's side.

    b.   If alone, (CALL 9-1-1) from your mobile device if you have one, and follow the dispatcher's instructions.

    c.   If alone without a mobile device, find a phone and (CALL 9-1-1), and get an AED if available.*

    * Correct any immediate life threats (such as opening the airway or controlling severe bleeding) before leaving an adult victim to call 9-1-1.

☐   **4.**   Check for normal breathing. If **no** breathing, begin CPR and use the AED as soon as available.

☐ Complete Skill

The Victim's History

Talk to a responsive victim or ask bystanders to find out more about what happened and the victim's condition. With a clear-cut injury, provide needed first aid before collecting the victim's history. The history can be important because it may identify the victim's condition needing first aid and because, if the victim later becomes unresponsive, the first aider may be the only person able to obtain this information.

The **SAMPLE** history format can help you remember the kinds of questions to ask:

S = Signs and symptoms

A = Allergies

M = Medications

P = Previous problems

L = Last food or drink

E = Events

A victim may be awake but confused. Ask the victim his or her name, where he or she is now, and for the time, day or date. The victim's answers reflect his or her mental status.

Example questions using **SAMPLE**:

S   How do you feel right now?

A   Are you allergic to any medications? To latex? To any foods? Or to insect stings, pollen, dust or grass?

M   Are you taking any prescribed medications? Which ones? What is the medication for? Did you take your medication today? Are you taking any over-the-counter medications, such as aspirin, cough syrup, vitamins or herbs? Have you recently started taking any new medications? Have you recently stopped taking any medications? Do you use any recreational drugs, such as cocaine or marijuana? Have you consumed any alcohol?

P   Are you seeing a doctor for any medical condition? Have you been in the hospital recently? Have you had any recent surgery? Have you ever experienced this issue before? Are these symptoms you have had before?

L   When is the last time you had something to eat or drink? What was it?

E   What were you doing before you started to feel this way? What events led up to this illness?

Give information about the victim's mental status and history to arriving EMS personnel.

Physical Examination of an Injured Victim

Unless you are giving first aid for a serious condition, check the victim thoroughly. In some cases, a victim's injury may not be obvious, or there may be multiple injuries. Unless you are certain there is only one obvious injury, examine an injured victim from head to toe, looking for anything out of the ordinary:

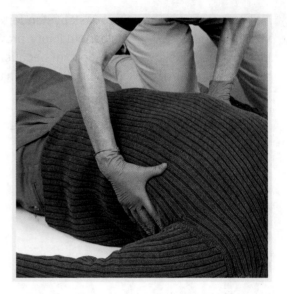

- Pain when an area is touched
- Bleeding or other wounds
- An area that is swollen or deformed
- Skin color (flushed or pale/ashen), temperature (hot or cold), condition (dry, sweating or clammy)
- Abnormal sensation or movement of the area
- A medical alert ID

Give first aid for any problems you find.

Module Summary: Checking a Victim

1. Ensure scene safety.
2. Check the victim for responsiveness.

(For a **responsive** victim:)

3. Ask the victim what happened and about their condition.
4. Have someone (CALL 9-1-1). If alone, correct any life-threatening conditions you see first (such as severe bleeding) before calling 9-1-1 and continuing to check the victim and providing other care.

(For an **unresponsive** victim:)

3. Call for help:
   a. Shout for someone to (CALL 9-1-1) and get an AED. Keep the phone at the victim's side.
   b. If alone, (CALL 9-1-1) from your mobile device if you have one, and follow the dispatcher's instructions.
   c. If alone without a mobile device, find a phone and call (CALL 9-1-1), and get an AED if available.*

   * Correct any immediate life threats (such as opening the airway or controlling severe bleeding) before leaving an adult victim to call 9-1-1.

4. Check for normal breathing. If **no** breathing, begin CPR and use the AED as soon as available.

Recovery Position

Objectives

- Identify the purpose of the recovery position.
- Demonstrate how to put an unresponsive breathing adult in the recovery position.

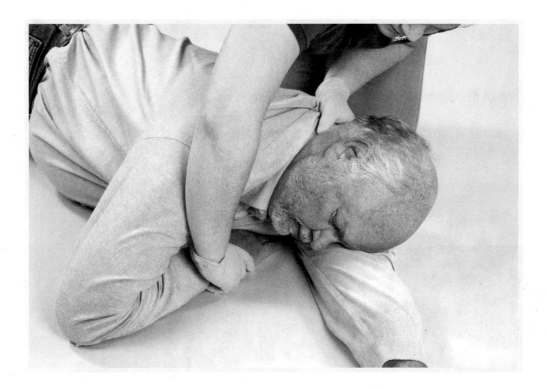

Video Review

Complete the following statement:

Use the recovery position for a victim who is _____ and

_____ .

What are the benefits of the recovery position? **Check all that apply.**

☐   It helps the heart beat more efficiently.

☐   It allows the person to breathe more easily.

☐   It allows fluids to drain from the mouth.

☐   It helps the body stay warm.

☐   It prevents inhalation of stomach contents if the victim vomits.

☐   It helps control bleeding of the extremities.

Recovery Position

Pair up with another person in the class to practice putting an unresponsive victim in the recovery position.

Performance Checklist

Skill Steps

☐ 1. Extend one of the victim's arms above the victim's head.

☐ 2. Carefully roll the victim's body onto its side so that the victim's head is supported on the extended arm.

☐ 3. Bend both legs so the victim's position is stabilized.

☐ 4. With victim now in position, open the mouth to allow drainage and monitor breathing.

☐ **Complete Skill**

Module Summary: Recovery Position

O Use the side-lying recovery position for any unresponsive victim who is breathing.

O **Do not** use the recovery position if the victim has experienced trauma, especially any trauma suggesting a neck, back, hip or pelvic injury.

Bleeding and Wound Care

Objectives

- Demonstrate how to control bleeding with direct pressure.
- Demonstrate how to apply a pressure bandage.
- Describe how to clean and dress a minor wound.
- List signs and symptoms of a wound infection.
- Identify when to seek medical attention for a wound.
- State when a tetanus booster is needed.
- Describe the care needed for internal bleeding.
- Recognize when bleeding is severe and needs special care.
- Explain when use of a tourniquet is appropriate for controlling severe bleeding.
- Explain how to control severe bleeding using a commercial tourniquet.
- Explain when wound packing is appropriate for controlling severe bleeding.
- Explain how to control severe bleeding with wound packing.
- Identify the care needed for a variety of wounds and injuries.

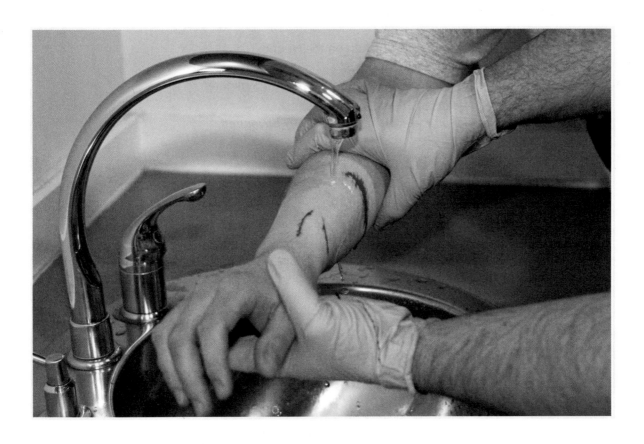

Bleeding Control

Video Review

Circle **True** or **False** for the following statement:

The most effective way to stop bleeding is to put firm pressure directly on a dressing over the wound with a gloved hand.

True   **False**

Bleeding Control

Learn the Skill

Pair up with a classmate to practice controlling bleeding in an extremity.

Performance Checklist

Skill Steps

☐ **1.** Put on gloves.
Improvise a barrier if no gloves are available.

☐ **2.** Place a sterile dressing or clean cloth on the wound.

☐ **3.** Apply firm, direct pressure with your hand for about 5 minutes.
Do not put pressure on an object in a wound.
Do not put pressure on the scalp if the skull may be injured.

☐ **4.** Re-evaluate the bleeding.

   a. If direct pressure **does not** control the bleeding and you have a hemostatic dressing, remove dressings already used and apply the hemostatic dressing directly on the wound using direct pressure.

   b. If a hemostatic dressing is **not** available, continue to apply direct pressure. If blood soaks through the first dressing, place additional dressings on top of the blood-soaked dressing and keep applying pressure.

☐ **5.** If needed, apply a pressure bandage to keep pressure on the wound, wrapping from the end of the extremity toward the center of the body.
The pressure is sufficient if the bandage is snug but you can slip a finger under it.
Use a tourniquet (if you are so trained) when direct pressure and a pressure bandage do not control severe bleeding from a limb.

☐ **6.** If appropriate, treat the victim for shock and (CALL 9-1-1).

☐ **Complete Skill**

Pressure Bandage

Learn the Skill

Pair up with a classmate to practice applying a pressure bandage to an extremity.

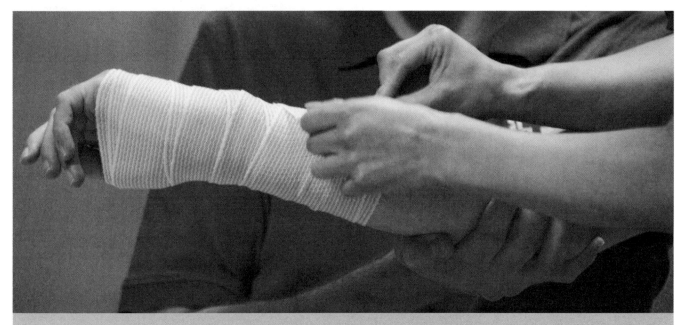

Performance Checklist

Skill Steps

☐ **1.** Anchor the starting end of the elastic or self-adhering bandage below the wound dressing.

☐ **2.** Make several circular turns.

☐ **3.** Work up the limb in overlapping turns.

☐ **4.** Fix or tie the end of the bandage in place.
The pressure is sufficient if the bandage is snug but a finger can be slipped under it.

☐ **Complete Skill**

Notes:

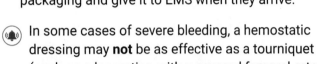

Hemostatic Dressings

- Hemostatic dressings are dressings treated with an agent that can help control bleeding.
- Hemostatic dressings can be used to control bleeding from an open wound when the bleeding cannot be controlled by direct pressure alone, or where use of a tourniquet is not possible.
- Hemostatic dressings should be applied directly on a wound with direct pressure or a pressure bandage, just like a regular dressing.
- If a hemostatic dressing is used, save the packaging and give it to EMS when they arrive.

🔔 In some cases of severe bleeding, a hemostatic dressing may **not** be as effective as a tourniquet (such as a laceration with a severed femoral artery or a small but deep laceration on the forearm). Hemostatic dressings are likely of greatest use for severe external bleeding in locations where standard pressure control is **not** effective, when a tourniquet **cannot** be applied (trunk or areas such as the abdomen, axilla, or groin), when a tourniquet is **not** available, or when a tourniquet is **not** effective to stop bleeding.

Wound Care

Video Review

Circle True or **False** for each of the following statements:

To clean a small wound once bleeding has stopped, pour rubbing alcohol on it.   **True**   **False**

A victim with a gaping wound or a deep puncture wound should seek medical attention.   **True**   **False**

How should you clean a wound with dirt in it?

_____

_____

When should you put an antibiotic ointment on a wound?

_____

_____

First Aid Steps for Wound Care

FIRST AID STEPS

1. Wash your hands and put on gloves if available.
2. Gently wash shallow wounds and abrasions with large amounts of warm or room-temperature water with or without soap to remove dirt.
3. Irrigate a deeper wound that is **not** severely bleeding under large amounts of running water to remove foreign matter.
4. **Do not** use alcohol, hydrogen peroxide or iodine on wound.
5. Pat area dry.
6. Apply antibiotic ointment only to an abrasion or superficial wound and only if the victim is **not** allergic to the antibiotic.
7. Cover the wound with a sterile dressing and bandage.
8. Seek medical attention for these wounds:
   - If the victim's tetanus vaccination is out of date
   - The wound may be infected.
   - A deep or puncture wound
   - An impaled object
   - A wound that may require stitches (cuts on the face or hands when the edges **do not** close together, gaping wounds and cuts longer than 1 inch).

Identify the Condition

What is likely wrong with this wounded finger?

_____

_____

_____

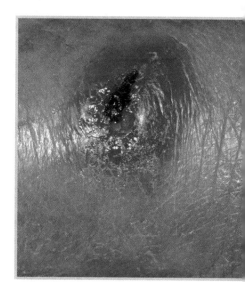

If your finger looked like this 4 days after being injured, what should you do?

_____

_____

_____

Care for Special Wounds

Puncture Wounds

FIRST AID STEPS

1. Irrigate the wound with large amounts of warm or room-temperature water with or without soap to remove foreign matter.
2. Gently press on wound edges to promote bleeding.
3. Dry the area. **Do not** put any medication inside or over the puncture wound.
4. Cover the wound with a sterile dressing and bandage.
5. Seek medical attention.

Impaled Object in Wound

FIRST AID STEPS

1. **Do not** remove the object, which could cause more bleeding and injury. Control bleeding by applying direct pressure around the edges of the object.
2. Dress the wound around the object.
3. Stabilize the object in place with large dressings or folded cloths.
4. Support the object while bandaging the dressings in place.
5. Keep the victim still and seek medical attention.

Head and Face Injuries

For any painful head injury and any head trauma in a child older than age 2, suspect a spinal injury and restrict movement of the head and spine.

Head Wounds (no skull fracture)

FIRST AID STEPS

1. Replace any skin flaps and cover the wound with a sterile dressing.
2. Use direct pressure to control bleeding.
3. Put a roller or triangle bandage around the victim's head to secure the dressing.
4. Seek medical attention if the victim later experiences nausea and vomiting, persistent headache, drowsiness or disorientation, stumbling or lack of coordination or problems with speech or vision.

Nose Bleeding or Injury

FIRST AID STEPS

1. Have the victim sit and tilt his or her head slightly forward with the mouth open. **Do not** let the victim lie down. Carefully remove any object you see protruding from the nose, but **do not** probe inside the nose.
2. Have the victim pinch the nostrils together just below the bridge of the nose for 10 minutes. Ask the victim to breathe through the mouth and to **not** speak, swallow, cough or sniff.
3. If the victim is gasping or choking on blood in the throat, (CALL 9-1-1).
4. Place a cold compress on the bridge of the nose.
5. After 10 minutes, release the pressure slowly. Pinch the nostrils again for 10 minutes if bleeding continues.
6. Seek medical attention if:
   - Bleeding continues after 2 attempts to control it.
   - You suspect the nose is broken.
   - A foreign object is in the nose.
   - The victim has a history of high blood pressure.
7. Have the victim rest for a few hours and avoid rubbing or blowing the nose.

Mouth Injuries

FIRST AID STEPS

1. Have the victim sit with the head tilted forward to let blood drain.
2. For a wound penetrating the lip: Put a rolled dressing between the lip and gum. Hold a second dressing against the outside lip.
3. For a bleeding tongue: Put a dressing on the wound and apply pressure.
4. **Do not** repeatedly rinse the mouth (this may prevent clotting).
5. **Do not** let the victim swallow blood (this may cause vomiting).
6. When the bleeding stops, tell the victim to **not** drink anything warm for several hours.
7. Seek medical attention if the bleeding is severe or **does not** stop.

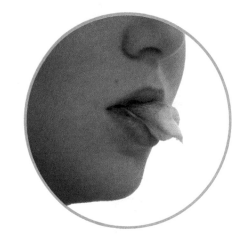

Notes:

Knocked Out Tooth (Dental Avulsion)

FIRST AID STEPS

1. Have the victim sit with his or her head tilted forward to let blood drain.
2. Rinse the wound with saline solution or tap water.
3. Control bleeding by having the victim bite down for 20-30 minutes on a gauze pad placed over the tooth socket.
4. Save the tooth. Pick it up by the crown but **do not** scrub or try to clean the tooth.
5. Place the tooth in a solution such as *Hank's Balanced Salt Solution*, propolis, egg white, coconut water, or whole milk. A specialized tooth-preserving solution can also be used. If these solutions are not available, wrap the tooth gently in a cling film to prevent dehydration and preserve the tooth for reimplantation. If none of these options are available, the tooth can be stored in cow's milk or saliva. **Do not** store the tooth in tap water.
6. Have the victim see a dental professional as soon as possible.

Object Impaled in the Cheek

FIRST AID STEPS

1. Check inside the mouth to see if the object has penetrated through.
2. If you can see both sides of the object and can remove it safely, gently pull the object out in the direction from which it penetrated the cheek, taking care with a sharp object **not** to cut the cheek further.
3. Place a dressing inside the mouth between the cheek wound and teeth; ensure the dressing **does not** come loose and block the airway.
4. Apply another dressing to the outside of the wound, applying pressure to control bleeding.
5. Position an unresponsive victim with the head turned to the side so blood and other fluid will run out of the mouth.

Open Chest Wounds

FIRST AID STEPS

1. Keep the victim still in the position found.
2. Cover an open wound with a sterile dressing and bandage. If an object is impaled in the wound, stabilize the object with bulky dressings. If you note air moving in or out of a penetrating chest wound, **do not** block the airflow with a dressing.
3. (CALL 9-1-1)

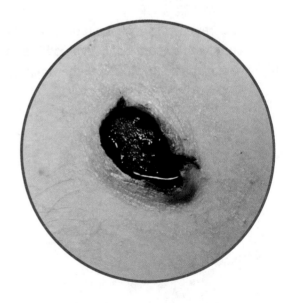

Abdominal Injuries

Closed Abdominal Injury

`SIGNS AND SYMPTOMS`

Severe pain or tenderness in area, victim protecting the abdomen, bruising, swollen or rigid abdomen, rapid shallow breathing, nausea or vomiting.

`FIRST AID STEPS`

1. Carefully position the victim on his or her back. Loosen tight clothing.
2. `CALL 9-1-1`
3. Treat for shock, monitor the victim's breathing and be ready to give CPR if needed.

Abdominal Injury – Internal Bleeding

`SIGNS AND SYMPTOMS`

Signs of severe internal bleeding include:

- Tender, swollen, bruised or hard abdomen
- Blood vomited or coughed up or present in urine
- Cool, clammy skin that may be pale or bluish

- Thirst
- Confusion
- Lightheadedness

`FIRST AID STEPS`

1. Have the victim lie down on his or her back.
2. `CALL 9-1-1`
3. Be alert for vomiting. Put a breathing victim who vomits or becomes unresponsive (if **no** suspected trauma, especially a neck, back, hip or pelvic injury) in the recovery position.
4. Keep the victim from becoming chilled or overheated.
5. **Do not** give the victim anything to drink.
6. If the victim becomes unresponsive, monitor his or her breathing and be ready to give CPR if needed.

🔔 Internal bleeding in the extremities will be covered later in Module 8: Bone, Joint and Muscle Injuries.

Open Abdominal Injury

`FIRST AID STEPS`

1. Position the victim on his or her back and loosen any tight clothing.
2. **Do not** push protruding organs back inside the abdomen. Cover the wound with a moist, sterile dressing or a dry, nonadherent dressing. **Do not** apply direct pressure on the wound.
3. Cover the dressing with a large occlusive dressing or plastic wrap taped loosely in place. **Then**, cover the area with a blanket or towel to help maintain warmth.
4. `CALL 9-1-1`
5. Treat the victim for shock. Monitor the victim's breathing and be ready to give CPR if needed.

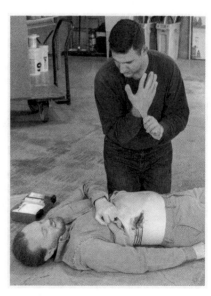

Severe Bleeding

Video Review

If you cannot control bleeding using direct pressure, a tourniquet can be used if severe bleeding occurs in an _____ or a _____.

If the victim has severe bleeding that cannot be managed with direct pressure occurs in an area where you can't apply a tourniquet, _____ should be performed if supplies are available.

Use of Tourniquets

A tourniquet can be used when you are unable to control bleeding in a limb with standard bleeding control (direct pressure with or without a dressing). Examples when a tourniquet may be appropriate:

- There are multiple victims to care for.
- The victim has multiple injuries requiring care.
- The environment becomes unsafe and you need to evacuate the victim.
- You are unable to access the wound.

🔔 Use a commercial tourniquet if available. Only apply a tourniquet if you are properly trained.

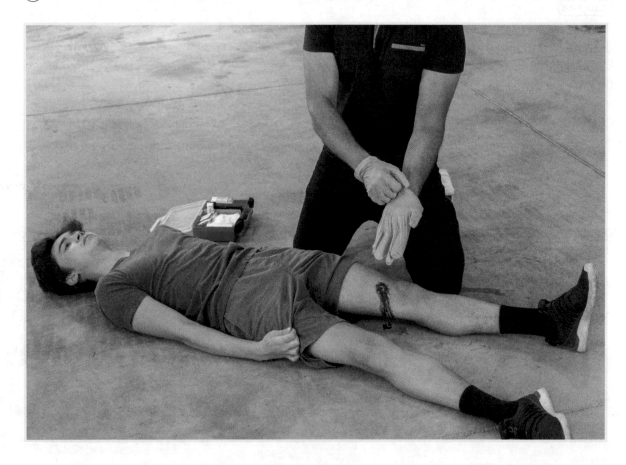

Using a Commercial Tourniquet

Learn the Skill

Pair up with a classmate to practice using a tourniquet to control severe bleeding.

Performance Checklist

Skill Steps

☐ **1.** Put on gloves (if you have not already done so).

☐ **2.** Assess the bleeding-If severe bleeding is coming from an injury on an arm or leg and it **cannot** be controlled with direct pressure apply a commercially available tourniquet.

☐ **3.** Remove the tourniquet from its package.

☐ **4.** Place the tourniquet around the limb approximately 2-3 inches above the wound.
   Be sure you do NOT place the tourniquet over a joint.

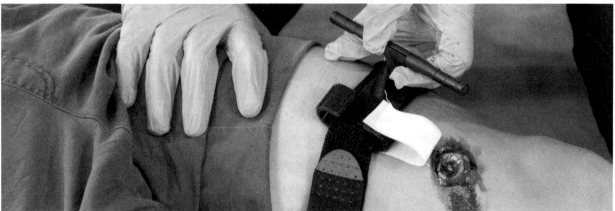

☐ **5.** Pull the free end of the tourniquet strap as tight as possible and secure the hook and loop fastener back on itself.
   Do not cover the windlass with the strap at this time.

☐ **6.** Twist the windlass until the bleeding stops. Then hook the end of the windlass into the windlass clip.

☐ **7.** Cover the windlass with the remaining end of the long strap.

☐ **8.** Secure the windlass retaining strap over the clip.
   Notice a place to write on the strap.

☐ **9.** Enter the time the tourniquet was applied on the retaining strap. Continue to monitor the patient and treat for shock until help arrives.

☐ Complete Skill

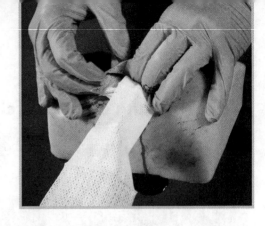

Wound Packing

Utilize wound packing and pressure application when the victim's bleeding is life-threatening and located on a body part that's **not** the arm or leg — such as the head, neck, chest or abdomen. You can also use wound packing in cases where the tourniquet **does not** stop the bleeding in the arm or leg of the victim. Packing the wound means taking material like gauze or clean cloth and placing it tightly **INTO** the wound. If hemostatic dressings are available use them to pack the wound. You **then** apply direct pressure until the bleeding stops before putting on a compression dressing.

FIRST AID STEPS

If severe bleeding **cannot** be controlled with direct pressure and you **do not** have access to a tourniquet or use of a tourniquet is **not** possible (such as on the neck, shoulder or groin) then you should:

1. Remove or cut away clothing that covers the wound.
2. Remove any **gauze** already on the wound and wipe away any pooled blood.
3. Pack the wound with hemostatic gauze (if available). If you **do not** have hemostatic gauze **then** pack the wound with plain sterile gauze or a clean cloth.
4. After packing the wound apply pressure with both hands, pushing as hard as you can.
5. Continue to apply pressure until medical help arrives to take over.

Wound Packing

Learn the Skill

Pair up with a classmate to practice wound packing to control severe bleeding.

Performance Checklist

Skill Steps

☐ 1. Put on gloves (if you have **not** already done so).

☐ 2. Assess the bleeding-If direct pressure with or without a hemostatic dressing **does not** control the bleeding remove the dressings already in place.

☐ 3. Pack the wound. This means stuff gauze or clean cloth into the wound. *If hemostatic dressings are available use them to pack the wound. If you do not have hemostatic dressings pack the wound with plain gauze or clean cloth.*

☐ 4. Apply hard, continuous pressure to the packed wound with both hands.

☐ 5. If the packing becomes soaked with blood — add more gauze or cloth on top of it.

☐ 6. Continue applying pressure until you are relieved by a medical professional.

☐ **Complete Skill**

Scenario 1: The Lunch Room

A coworker has cut her forearm badly with a knife in the lunch room. Another employee calls 9-1-1 and runs for the first aid kit while you help the victim. You do not have gloves with you. **What can you do to control the bleeding?**

_____

_____

_____

Module Summary: First Aid for Bleeding and Wound Care
FIRST AID STEPS

1. Control bleeding with firm pressure directly on the wound.

2. If needed, use a pressure bandage to maintain pressure to control bleeding.

3. A hemostatic dressing or tourniquet (if you are so trained) may be used if direct pressure **does not** control severe bleeding.

4. Clean a wound that is **not** severely bleeding under large amounts of running water.

5. Leave open chest wounds uncovered.

6. (CALL 9-1-1) for any serious injury and bleeding.

Additional Reference

Amputations

FIRST AID STEPS

1. (CALL 9-1-1)

2. Control bleeding and care for the victim's wound first, then recover and care for amputated part:

   a. Wrap the severed part in a dry sterile dressing or clean cloth. **Do not** wash it.

   b. Place the part in a plastic bag and seal it.

   c. Place the sealed bag in another bag or container with ice. **Do not** let the part touch ice directly or surround it with ice.

   d. Give the severed part to emergency personnel.

Genital Injuries

FIRST AID STEPS

1. Provide privacy for the victim.
2. Use direct pressure to control external bleeding.
3. For injured testicles, provide support with a towel positioned between the legs like a diaper.
4. For vaginal bleeding, have the woman press a sanitary pad or clean folded towel to the area.
5. (CALL 9-1-1) for severe or continuing bleeding, significant pain or swelling or the possibility of sexual abuse.

Eye Injuries

Blow to the Eye

FIRST AID STEPS

1. If the eye is bleeding or leaking fluid, (CALL 9-1-1), or get the victim to the emergency department immediately.
2. Put a cold pack over the eye for 15 minutes to ease pain and reduce swelling, but **do not** put pressure on the eye. If the victim is wearing a contact lens, **do not** remove it.
3. Have the victim lie still; cover the uninjured eye. Movement of the uninjured eye causes movement of the injured one.
4. Seek medical attention if pain persists or vision is **affected in any way.**

Chemical or Other Substance Splashed in the Eye

FIRST AID STEPS

1. Continuously flush the victim's eye with large amounts of clean running water for at least 15 minutes or until EMS arrives. If tap water is not available, use normal saline or a commercial eye irrigation solution.
2. Have a victim wearing contact lenses remove them.
3. Tilt the victim's head so the water does not run into the unaffected eye.
4. For a responsive victim, call the Poison Control Center **(800) 222-1222** immediately and follow its instructions. If a Control Center is not available, (CALL 9-1-1) or seek help from a medical provider.

Large Object Embedded in the Eye

FIRST AID STEPS

1. **Do not** remove the object. Stabilize it in place with dressings or bulky cloth.
2. Cover both eyes. Movement of the uninjured eye causes movement of the injured one.
3. (CALL 9-1-1) or get the victim to the emergency department immediately.

Small Particle in the Eye

FIRST AID STEPS

1. **Do not** let the victim rub the eye.
2. Gently pull the upper eyelid out and down over the lower eyelid.
3. If the particle remains, gently flush the eye with water from a medicine dropper or water glass. To keep water from flowing into the unaffected eye, position the victim's head so the affected eye is lower than the other eye.
4. If the particle remains and is visible, carefully try to brush it out with a sterile dressing. Lift the upper eyelid and swab its underside if you see the particle.
5. If the particle still remains or if the victim has any vision problems or pain, cover the eye with a sterile dressing and seek medical attention. Also, cover the uninjured eye. Movement of the uninjured eye causes movement of the injured one.

Ear Injuries

FIRST AID STEPS

1. **CALL 9-1-1** if you see clear fluid or watery blood coming from the ear.
2. Help the victim sit up and tilt the affected ear lower to let any fluid drain out.
3. Apply a loose sterile dressing. **Do not** apply pressure. **Do not** plug the ear closed.
4. Seek medical attention if 9-1-1 was **not** called.

Animal or Human Bites

FIRST AID STEPS

1. Clean the wound with large amounts of warm or room-temperature water with or without soap.
2. Control bleeding.
3. Cover the wound with a sterile dressing and bandage.
4. Seek medical attention immediately.
5. **Do not** try to catch the animal, but note its appearance and describe it to the health care provider.

Crush Injuries

FIRST AID STEPS

A crush injury is caused when strong pressure is exerted against the body. Depending on the force involved, a crushing injury can result in muscle, bone, nerve and tissue damage, shock and internal and/or external bleeding.

1. **CALL 9-1-1**
2. Provide care for the injuries you find.

6 Shock

Objectives

- List the causes of shock.
- Identify the signs and symptoms of shock.
- Describe the first aid for shock.
- Demonstrate how to put a victim in the shock position.

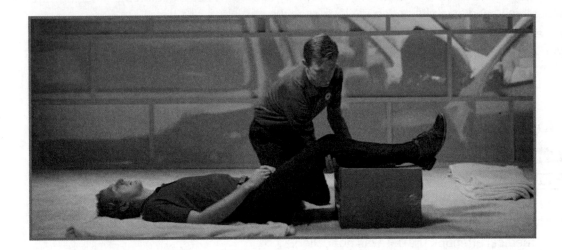

 ## Video Review

Complete the following statements:

The skin of a victim in shock is typically _____ and
_____ .

Have a victim in shock lie **down, and** then raise his or her _____
if there is no evidence of trauma.

Notes:

Shock Position

Learn the Skill

Pair up with a classmate to practice putting a victim in the shock position.

Performance Checklist

Skill Steps

☐ 1. Check for responsiveness, normal breathing and severe bleeding or injuries.

☐ 2. (CALL 9-1-1) and care first for life-threatening conditions, such as severe bleeding.

☐ 3. Be ready to give CPR if needed.

☐ 4. a. If there is **no** evidence of trauma, position a responsive victim on his or her back using a blanket or coat as a pad. If the movement or position **does not** cause the victim pain, raise the legs such that the feet are 6-12 inches above the ground.

   b. Put a breathing, unresponsive victim (if no suspected trauma, especially a neck, back, hip or pelvic injury) in the recovery position.

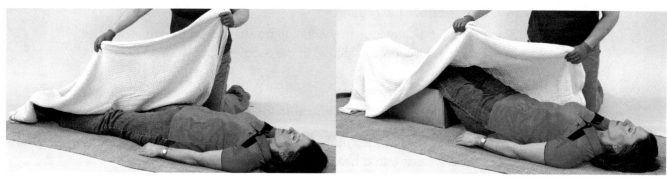

| Shock position | Shock position (non-trauma only) |

☐ 5. Loosen any tight clothing.

☐ 6. Be alert for the possibility of vomiting; turn the victim's head to drain the mouth.

☐ 7. Try to maintain the victim's normal body temperature. If necessary, maintain the victim's body heat with a blanket or coat over the victim.

☐ 8. **Do not** let a shock victim eat, drink or smoke.

☐ 9. Stay with the victim and offer reassurance and comfort.

☐ **Complete Skill**

Module Summary: First Aid for Shock

SIGNS AND SYMPTOMS

O   Anxiety, confusion, agitation or restlessness

O   Dizziness, lightheadedness

O   Cool, clammy or sweating skin that is pale, bluish or ashen in color

O   Rapid, shallow breathing

O   Thirst

O   Nausea, vomiting

O   Changing levels of consciousness

FIRST AID STEPS

1.   Check for responsiveness, normal breathing and severe bleeding or injuries.

2.   (CALL 9-1-1) and care first for life-threatening conditions, such as severe bleeding.

3.   Be ready to give CPR if needed.

4.   a.   If there is no evidence of trauma, position a responsive victim on his or her back using a blanket or coat as a pad. If the movement or position **does not** cause the victim pain, raise the legs, such that the feet are 6-12 inches above the ground.

    b.   Put a breathing, unresponsive victim (if no suspected trauma, especially a neck, back, hip or pelvic injury) in the recovery position.

5.   Loosen any tight clothing.

6.   Be alert for the possibility of vomiting; turn the victim's head to drain the mouth.

7.   Try to maintain the victim's normal body temperature. If necessary, maintain the victim's body heat with a blanket or coat over the victim.

8.   **Do not** let a shock victim eat, drink or smoke.

9.   Stay with the victim and offer reassurance and comfort.

Notes:

Burns

Objectives

- Differentiate among first-, second- and third-degree burns.
- Explain first aid for first-, second- and third-degree heat burns.
- Explain first aid for chemical burns.
- Identify first aid for electrical burns and shocks.

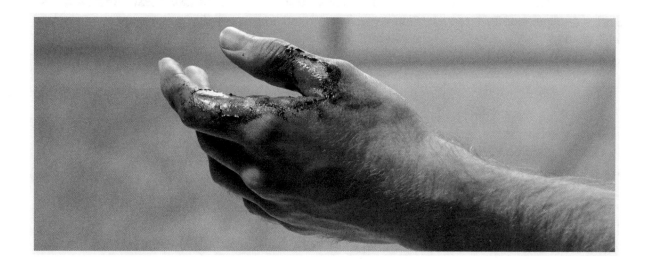

 ## Video Review

What are the first things you do for a serious burn?

_____

_____

Why would you not put water on a burn that covers more than 20% of the body?

_____

_____

How long should you flush the skin with water for a chemical burn?

_____

_____

Differences in Burns

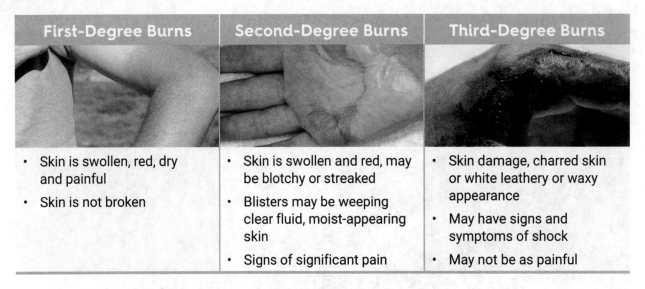

First-Degree Burns	Second-Degree Burns	Third-Degree Burns
• Skin is swollen, red, dry and painful • Skin is not broken	• Skin is swollen and red, may be blotchy or streaked • Blisters may be weeping clear fluid, moist-appearing skin • Signs of significant pain	• Skin damage, charred skin or white leathery or waxy appearance • May have signs and symptoms of shock • May not be as painful

Burn Prevention

- In the home, children and the elderly are most susceptible — protect them from all sources of heat or flame.
- Install smoke detectors throughout your home.
- Help prevent sunburn and skin cancer by using sunscreen or sunblock.

Poisonous Fumes and Chemicals

Number these actions in the correct order for a victim who has inhaled poisonous fumes from a fire.

_____ Loosen tight clothing around the neck or chest.

_____ Get the victim to fresh air.

_____ (CALL 9-1-1)

Circle Yes or **No** for the following statement:

In your home or at work, do you work with any chemicals or liquids likely to cause a burn if splashed on you?   **Yes**   **No**

If so, what would you do if this substance splashed in your eyes?

_____

_____

Inhaled Poison

SIGNS AND SYMPTOMS

Of carbon monoxide or other inhaled poison: Headache, dizziness, lightheadedness, confusion, weakness, nausea, vomiting, chest pain, convulsions, changing levels of responsiveness.

FIRST AID STEPS

1. Immediately move the victim into fresh air.
2. (CALL 9-1-1) even if the victim starts to recover.
3. Monitor the victim's breathing and be ready to give CPR if needed.
4. Put an unresponsive, breathing victim in the Recovery Position.
5. Loosen tight clothing around the neck or chest.

Scenario 1: A Burned Arm

Your friend has just burned his arm at a barbecue – it looks like a small second-degree burn. You grab a nearby hose and cool the burned area with cool or cold running water. Then you get your first aid kit. **What do you do next?**

_____

_____

_____

Scenario 2: Chemical Spill

You enter an outdoor storage area where you work and find a coworker frantically trying to rub a white powder from his arm. Beside him on the ground is a broken container that is leaking a chemical. **What are the first aid steps to follow?**

_____

_____

_____

Module Summary:

First Aid for First- and Second-Degree Burns

SIGNS AND SYMPTOMS

o First-degree burns: skin is red, dry and painful; swelling; skin is not broken.

o Second-degree burns: skin is swollen and red; skin may be blotchy or streaked; blisters are present and possibly weeping clear fluid; pain is significant.

FIRST AID STEPS

1. Stop the burning by removing the heat source.

2. Immediately cool the burn with running cool or cold potable water, such as tap water, for at least 10 minutes. (**Do not** put ice on a burn, which could cause tissue injury.)

3. Remove constricting items, such as clothing and jewelry.

4. For large second-degree burns, (CALL 9-1-1).

5. Protect the burn area from friction or pressure. Put a sterile, dry dressing over the burn to protect the area, but keep it loose and **do not** tape it to the skin.

6. Keep burn blisters intact. This reduces pain and improves healing by preventing infection. Natural remedies, such as honey or potato peel dressings, should **not** be applied to a burn.

7. Seek medical attention for burns on the face, neck, genitals, hands, or feet and for burns involving blistering or broken skin, difficulty breathing, a large surface area or other causes for concern.

First Aid for Third-Degree Burns

SIGNS AND SYMPTOMS

o Damaged, charred or white leathery skin. Watch also for signs and symptoms of shock: clammy, pale or ashen skin; nausea and vomiting; fast breathing.

FIRST AID STEPS

1. Stop the burning by removing the heat source.

2. Immediately cool the burn with running cool or cold potable water, such as tap water, for at least 10 minutes. (**Do not** put ice on a burn, which could cause tissue injury.) **Do not** attempt to cool the burn with cool or cold water if it is larger than 20% of the body (e.g., one whole leg or torso from neck to waist) or 10% for child because of the risk of hypothermia and shock. With a large burn, monitor the victim for hypothermia.

3. Remove clothing and jewelry **before** the area swells.

4. (CALL 9-1-1)

5. Treat for shock: Have victim lie on back, elevate legs if trauma is not suspected and maintain normal body temperature.

6. Carefully cover the burn with a sterile, dry dressing; keep it loose and **do not** tape to skin; **do not** apply cream or ointment.

7. **Do not** give the victim anything to drink.

8. Watch the victim's breathing and be ready to give CPR if needed.

Module Summary:

First Aid for Chemical Burns

FIRST AID STEPS

1. Check the Safety Data Sheet (SDS) for the chemical involved.

2. Move the victim away from fumes or ventilate the area.

3. With a gloved hand or piece of cloth, brush off any dry chemical.

4. Remove clothing and jewelry from the burn area.

5. Flush the entire area as quickly as possible with large amounts of running water. Flush until EMS personnel arrive to give definitive care or until a toxic-specific solution is available.

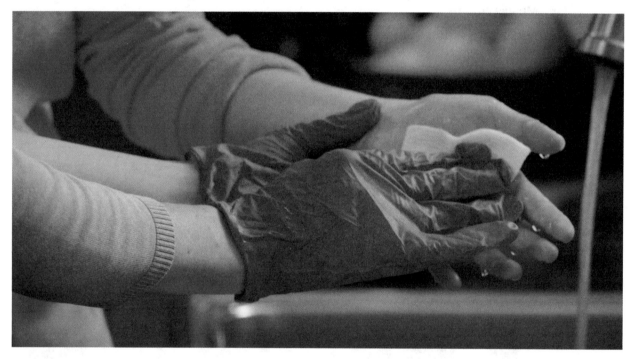

6. (CALL 9-1-1)

Notes:

Bone, Joint and Muscle Injuries

Objectives

- Demonstrate how to apply an elastic bandage.
- Identify first aid for:
  - Fractures
  - Dislocations
  - Sprains
  - Bruises
  - Broken ribs
  - Hip injuries
  - Muscle strains
  - Muscle cramps
- Explain how to use rest, ice, compression and elevation (RICE) for an injury.
- Describe different types of splints.
- Identify when it is appropriate to splint.

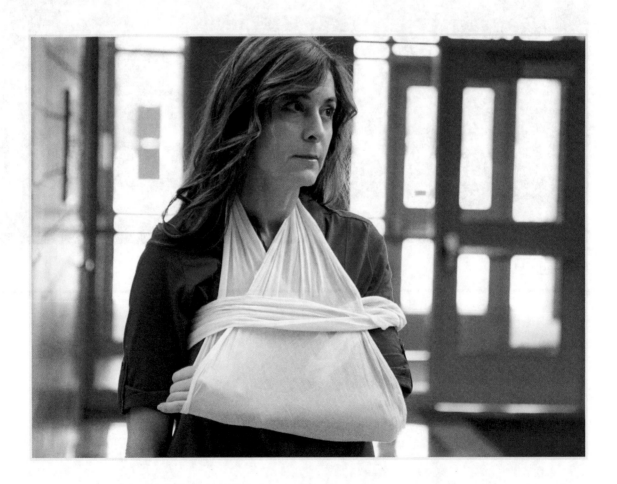

Video Review

The signs and symptoms of a bone or joint injury include which of the following?
Check all that apply.

☐ Deformed area   ☐ Small or unequal pupils

☐ Skin is hot and red   ☐ Swelling

☐ Pain   ☐ Inability to use body part

☐ Fever

Write out the meaning of **RICE**:

R = _____

I = _____

C = _____

E = _____

When is it necessary to (CALL 9-1-1) for a bone, joint or muscle injury?

_____

_____

_____

_____

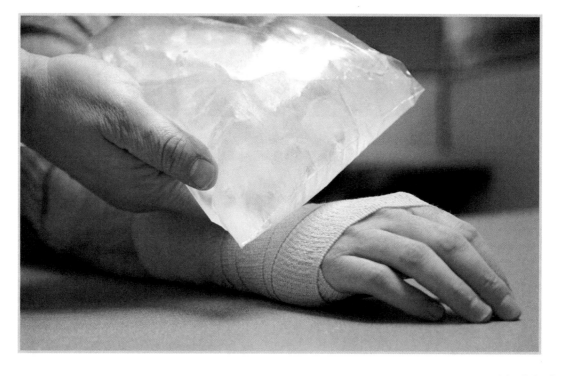

Applying an Elastic Bandage

Learn the Skill

Pair up with a classmate to practice applying an elastic bandage around the wrist.

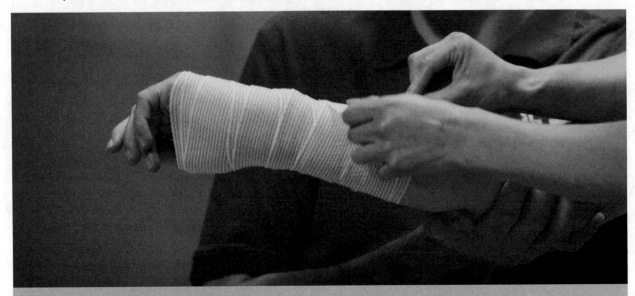

Performance Checklist

Skill Steps

☐ 1. Anchor the starting end of the bandage.

☐ 2. Turn the bandage diagonally across the wrist and back around the hand (forming a figure 8).

☐ 3. Continue overlapping the figure-8 turns by about ¾ of the previous turn.

☐ 4. Secure or fasten the end of the bandage, such as with clips or tape.

☐ **Complete Skill**

Notes:

Creating an Arm Sling and Binder

Learn the Skill

Pair up with a classmate to practice creating an arm sling and binder.

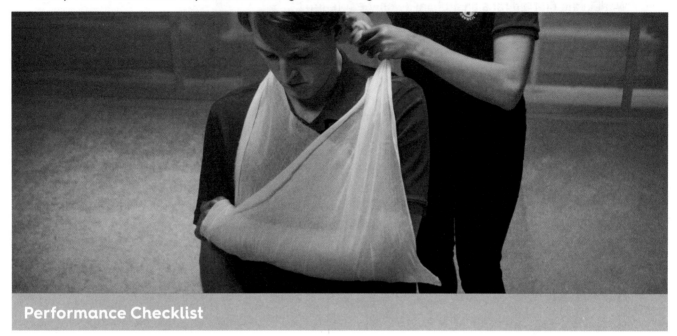

Performance Checklist

Skill Steps

☐   **1.**   Secure the point of the bandage at the elbow. Use a safety pin or tie the point at the elbow.

☐   **2.**   Position the triangular bandage while the victim supports the arm.

☐   **3.**   Bring up the lower end of the bandage to the opposite side of the neck.

☐   **4.**   Tie the ends. Pad under the knot.

☐   **5.**   Tie a binder over the sling and around the chest to help prevent movement.

☐ **Complete Skill**

Sprains

How long should ice be kept on a sprain or other injury? **Complete the following statement.**

Keep the ice on for _____ minutes (or _____ minutes if it produces discomfort),

then remove it for _____ minutes. Reapply it for _____ minutes (or _____ minutes

if it produces discomfort), and then remove it for _____ minutes.

Bruises

A bruise is a sign of bleeding from damaged blood vessels under the skin. Bruises can occur in both minor and more severe injuries.

What is the first aid for a painful bruise on the forearm?

_____

_____

FIRST AID STEPS

• First, treat the injury that caused the bruising.
• For pain relief, apply cold to the bruised area. Place a plastic bag or damp cloth with an ice-water mix on the injured area to reduce swelling and pain; put a barrier, such as a cloth, between the plastic bag and the skin. A cold pack also can be used. Apply the cold for 20 minutes (or 10 minutes if it produces discomfort), then remove it for 30 minutes; reapply for 20 (or 10) minutes, then remove again for 30 minutes.

Splinting

When to Splint

• Splint an injury if help will be delayed and there is a risk of the injured area moving.
• Splint an injury of the hand or foot if the victim is to be transported to the hospital in a personal vehicle.
• **Do not** move or try to straighten an injured extremity.

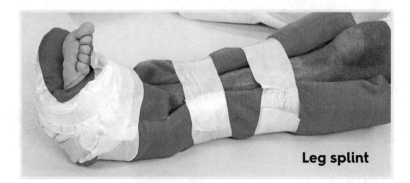

Leg splint

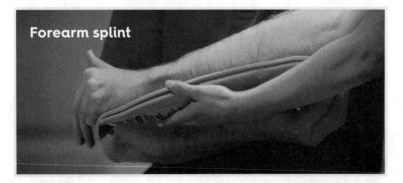

Forearm splint

Rib Injuries

Rib or other chest injuries are most serious when they threaten breathing.

FIRST AID STEPS

1. Help the victim into a position for **easiest breathing.**
2. Support the ribs with a pillow or **soft padding** loosely bandaged over the area and under the arm.
3. (CALL 9-1-1)
4. Monitor the victim's breathing while waiting for help.
5. If helpful, immobilize the arm with an arm sling and binder to prevent movement and ease pain.

Hip Injuries

An elderly woman slips and falls. She says she has terrible pain in one hip. She is pale, her skin is cool and clammy and she is becoming confused. **What should you do immediately?**

_____

_____

_____

In addition to the hip injury, what life-threatening condition is this woman probably **experiencing?**
Check the best answer.

☐ Cardiac arrest   ☐ Stroke   ☐ Shock   ☐ Anaphylaxis

What else can you do for her while waiting for help to arrive?

_____

_____

_____

First Aid for a Hip Injury

FIRST AID STEPS

1. (CALL 9-1-1)
2. If help may be delayed, immobilize the victim's legs by padding and bandaging them together, unless this causes more pain.
3. Treat for Shock. Monitor the victim's breathing and be ready to give CPR if needed.

Module 8 - Bone, Joint and Muscle Injuries

Muscle Cramps and Strains

What would you do for a muscle cramp?

_____

_____

What would you do for a muscle strain?

_____

_____

🔔 Always remember the acronym **RICE** for these and other injuries of bones, joints and muscles.

Scenario 1: An Incident at Work

At the loading dock at work, you see a worker who was struck by a large piece of equipment that fell off a forklift. The worker is lying on the ground in obvious pain when you approach. His forearm seems bent, and when you carefully cut through the bloody shirt sleeve, you find a wound in which you can see the end of a broken bone. The wound is still bleeding.

What should you do? (List at least 4 appropriate actions.)

_____

_____

_____

_____

_____

_____

Scenario 2: Stairway Fall

A coworker loses his footing coming down the last 2 steps of a stairway and falls forward, breaking his fall with an outstretched arm. He calls for help, and you find him sitting on the bottom step, using his left hand to hold his right forearm close to his body. He tells you his right shoulder really hurts and he cannot move it. He is wearing a thick shirt, and you cannot see whether there is any swelling or deformity, but there is apparently no bleeding. You ask someone to (CALL 9-1-1).

What else should you do before help arrives? Circle **Yes** for each action you should take or **No** for each action you should not take.

Have him straighten his arm so you can remove his shirt.	Yes	No
Immediately splint the arm with a board.	Yes	No
Immobilize and support the arm and shoulder in the position found.	Yes	No
Ask the victim if he is able to walk to your car to go to the hospital.	Yes	No
Put an ice bag or cold pack on the painful injured area.	Yes	No
Watch for signs and symptoms of shock.	Yes	No
Elevate the arm over his head.	Yes	No

Module Summary: First Aid for Bone, Joint and Muscle Injuries
FIRST AID STEPS

1. You **do not** need to know the exact type of bone, joint or muscle injury to give first aid.

2. (CALL 9-1-1) for any serious injury, large bone fracture or dislocation.

3. Help prevent movement of the injured area.

4. Follow the **RICE** acronym for most injuries of bones, joints and muscles.

5. With serious injuries, monitor the victim's breathing and be prepared to treat for shock.

Notes:

9 Head and Spine Injuries

Objectives

- Identify situations when a spinal injury is possible.
- Demonstrate spinal motion restriction for spinal injuries.
- Describe first aid for skull fractures.
- Describe first aid for general head wounds.
- Describe first aid for concussion.

▶ Video Review

List some risk factors that would cause you to suspect a spinal injury.

_____

_____

Which of the following are actions you should take for a victim with a suspected spinal injury? **Check all that apply.**

- ☐ Avoid touching the victim anywhere.
- ☐ **Have someone** (CALL 9-1-1).
- ☐ **Put the victim's head on a pillow to be in line with the spine.**
- ☐ Hold the victim's head and neck in the position found.
- ☐ Place ice bags all over and around the neck.
- ☐ Drive the victim to a hospital emergency department as soon as possible.

Notes:

Spinal Injury

SIGNS AND SYMPTOMS

Suspect a spinal injury in an injured victim who has these risk factors:

- Victim is 65 or older.
- Motor vehicle or bicycle crash involving driver, passenger or pedestrian
- Falls from more than the person's standing height
- Victim feels tingling in hands or feet, pain in back or neck, or muscle weakness or lack of feeling in torso or arms.

FIRST AID STEPS

1. Ask a responsive victim what happened. If he or she has any of the risk factors, explain the need to hold the head still to prevent spinal movement. With an unresponsive victim, check for risk factors for suspected spinal injury.
2. Hold the victim's head and neck with both hands in the position found to prevent movement of the neck and spine.
3. Assess the victim's breathing and be ready to give CPR if needed.
4. Have someone (CALL 9-1-1).
5. Reassure a conscious victim and tell him or her not to move.
6. Continue to stabilize head/spine and monitor the victim's breathing until help arrives.

Spinal Motion Restriction

Pair up with a classmate to practice spinal motion restriction.

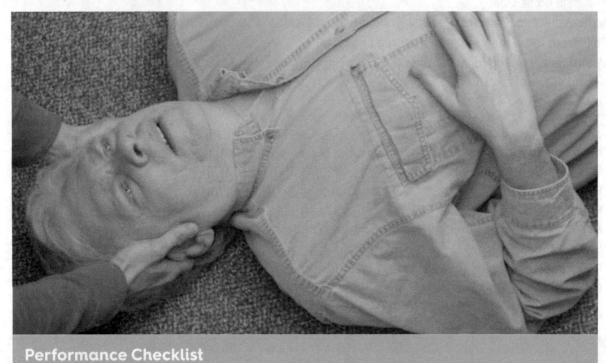

Performance Checklist

Skill Steps

☐ **1.** Ask a responsive victim what happened. If he or she has any of the risk factors, explain the need to hold the head still to restrict spinal movement. With an unresponsive victim, check for risk factors for suspected spinal injury.

☐ **2.** Hold the victim's head and neck with both hands in the position found to restrict movement of the neck and spine.

☐ **3.** Assess the victim's breathing and be ready to give CPR if needed.

☐ **4.** Have someone (CALL 9-1-1).

☐ **5.** Reassure a conscious victim and tell him or her **not** to move.

☐ **6.** Continue to stabilize the head and spine, and monitor the victim's breathing until help arrives.

☐ **Complete Skill**

Video Review

List signs and symptoms of a concussion.

_____

_____

_____

_____

_____

Which of the following are actions you should take for a victim of a head wound without a skull fracture? **Check all that apply.**

☐ Use direct pressure to control bleeding.

☐ Keep any skin flaps open.

☐ Put a roller or triangle bandage around the victim's head to secure any dressing.

☐ Place ice bags all over and around the head.

☐ Seek medical attention if any of the victim's symptoms worsen.

Head Injuries

If you notice a deformed or depressed area on the victim's skull or if there is fluid coming from the victim's ears or nose, suspect a skull fracture.

FIRST AID STEPS

1. Put a breathing, unresponsive victim in the recovery position unless there may be a neck, back, hip or pelvic injury. Monitor breathing and be ready to give CPR if needed.
2. **Do not** clean the wound, press on it, or remove an impaled object.
3. Cover the wound with a sterile dressing.
4. If there is significant bleeding, apply pressure only around the edges of the wound, **not** on the wound itself. **Do not** apply pressure if you feel bone fragments move.
5. **Do not** move the victim unnecessarily because there may also be a spinal injury.
6. (CALL 9-1-1) and stay with the victim.

Circle True or **False** for each of the following statements:

Before bandaging the wound, you should remove an impaled object from a victim's head. **True** **False**

Put all skull fracture victims in the recovery position. **True** **False**

Skull Fracture

SIGNS AND SYMPTOMS

Deformed area of the skull; depressed area in bone felt by touch; blood or fluid coming from ears or nose.

FIRST AID STEPS

1. Put a breathing, unresponsive victim in the Recovery Position unless there may be a neck, back, hip or pelvic injury. Monitor breathing and be ready to give CPR if needed.
2. **Do not** clean the wound, press on it or remove an impaled object.
3. Cover the wound with a sterile dressing.
4. If there is significant bleeding, apply pressure only around the edges of the wound, **not** on the wound itself. **Do not** apply pressure if you feel bone fragments move.
5. **Do not** move the victim unnecessarily because there may also be a spinal injury.
6. (CALL 9-1-1) and stay with the victim.

Concussion

SIGNS AND SYMPTOMS

Concussion is a brain injury that can result from a blow to the head or from sudden, violent movement of the head, such as in whiplash.

FIRST AID STEPS

1. Encourage the victim to rest, and avoid physical activity or activities that could cause additional head trauma.
2. The victim should **not** take any pain reliever unless directed by a health care provider.
3. The victim should be evaluated by a health care provider before resuming physical activity.
4. If the victim's symptoms are severe or become worse, (CALL 9-1-1) or seek medical attention immediately.

Circle True or **False** for each of the following statements:

Before calling 9-1-1, wait an hour or two after a head injury to see if concussion symptoms develop.

True   False

Just feeling dazed and confused after a blow to the head is normal and not a sign of concussion.

True   False

Scenario 1: Coworker Struck in the Head

A coworker was struck in the head by a piece of machinery and is lying on the floor when you find him. He is breathing, and his scalp is bleeding over one ear. You put on gloves and gently touch the bleeding area with a piece of gauze. You feel a small depressed area in the skull bone.

What must you avoid doing when you try to control the bleeding?

_____

How can you control the bleeding?

_____

Should you move this victim to look for other injuries to his body? Why, or why not?

_____

Module Summary:

First Aid for Spinal Motion Restriction

FIRST AID STEPS

1. Ask a responsive victim what happened. If he or she has any of the risk factors, explain the need to hold the head still to restrict spinal movement. With an unresponsive victim, check for risk factors for suspected spinal injury.

2. Hold the victim's head and neck with both hands in the position found to restrict movement of the neck and spine.

3. Assess the victim's breathing and be ready to give CPR if needed.

4. Have someone (CALL 9-1-1).

5. Reassure a conscious victim and tell him or her **not** to move.

6. Continue to stabilize the head and spine, and monitor the victim's breathing until help arrives.

First Aid for Head Injuries

Concussion

FIRST AID STEPS

1. Encourage the victim to rest and avoid physical activity or activities that could cause additional head trauma.

2. The victim should **not** take any pain reliever unless directed by a health care provider.

3. The victim should be evaluated by a health care provider before resuming physical activity.

4. If the victim's symptoms are severe or become worse, (CALL 9-1-1) or seek medical attention immediately.

Skull Fracture

FIRST AID STEPS

1. Put a breathing, unresponsive victim in the recovery position unless there may be a spinal injury. Monitor breathing and be ready to give CPR if needed.

2. **Do not** clean the wound, press on it or remove an impaled object.

3. Cover the wound with a sterile dressing.

4. If there is significant bleeding, apply pressure only around the edges of the wound, **not** on the wound itself. **Do not** apply pressure if you feel bone fragments move.

5. **Do not** move the victim unnecessarily, because there may also be a spinal injury.

6. (CALL 9-1-1) and stay with the victim.

10 Sudden Illness

Objectives

- Describe the general signs and symptoms of sudden illness.
- List the general steps of first aid for sudden illness.
- Describe the signs and symptoms of a heart attack.
- List the general steps of first aid for a heart attack.
- Identify the first aid steps for different sudden illnesses, including:
  - Stroke
  - Asthma
  - Breathing difficulty
  - Hypoglycemia and diabetic emergencies
  - Fainting
  - Presyncope
  - Abdominal pain
  - Seizures

Sudden Illness

▶ Video Review

What can you do for a victim of any sudden illness if you do not recognize the specific problem?

_____

_____

_____

_____

Heart Attack

▶ Video Review

List as many of the possible heart attack signs and symptoms as you can.

_____

_____

When should you (CALL 9-1-1) for a possible heart attack?

_____

_____

What first aid can you provide for a possible heart attack?

_____

_____

Notes:

First Aid for a Heart Attack

SIGNS AND SYMPTOMS

Victims frequently deny having a heart attack. Heart attack signs and symptoms can vary widely, and victims having a heart attack may not have all of these signs and symptoms. **Do not** depend only on the classic signs and symptoms, especially in women. In men and women, the most common symptom is chest pain or discomfort. However, women are more likely than men to experience shortness of breath, indigestion, nausea or vomiting, and back or jaw pain.

🔔 **Remember**, heart attack is a common sudden illness. (CALL 9-1-1) immediately when you see its signs and symptoms.

Angina

Angina is a medical condition that also causes chest pain and that a first aider may confuse with heart attack. The chest pain of angina usually happens after intense activity or exertion, is recognized as angina by the victim, and lasts only a few minutes. It is vitally important that you treat related signs and symptoms as a heart attack unless the victim has been diagnosed with angina and recognizes the symptoms as angina pain.

SIGNS AND SYMPTOMS

- Ask if the person has been diagnosed with angina and if the pain is like angina pain experienced in the past. If so, help the person take his or her own medication and rest.
- (CALL 9-1-1) and give heart attack first aid if:
  - The pain lasts longer than 10 minutes
  - The pain goes away but **then** comes back
  - The person has other heart attack symptoms **not** relieved by rest

Stroke

 ### Video Review

Which of the following are signs and symptoms that someone may be having a stroke? **Check all that apply.**

- ☐ High fever
- ☐ Bleeding from the nose and ears
- ☐ Sudden hunger
- ☐ Deformity in the extremities
- ☐ Numbness of face or arm on one side
- ☐ Rapid muscle twitches
- ☐ Slurred speech

Complete the following statement:

The single most important thing to do for a stroke victim is to _____ .

How should you position a responsive stroke victim while waiting for help to arrive? **Select the best answer.**

a. Have the victim keep walking.

b. Put the victim in the shock position with feet slightly raised.

c. Have the victim lie on his or her back with head and shoulders slightly raised.

d. Have the victim sit and put his or her head between their knees.

First Aid for a Stroke

SIGNS AND SYMPTOMS

The acronym, **FAST**, is an easy way to remember how to recognize a stroke. **Write** in the steps to take for each of the FAST actions:

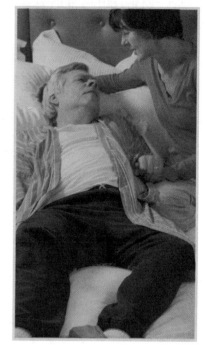

F	Face Drooping	
A	Arm Weakness	
S	Speech Difficulty	
T	Time to (CALL 9-1-1)	

It is very important to (CALL 9-1-1) as soon as you recognize that someone is having a stroke, since the chance of survival and recovery is greatest if the victim receives medical treatment as soon as possible after she was last seen feeling and acting normally.

Asthma

 Video Review

What are the common signs and symptoms of asthma?

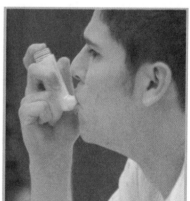

_____

_____

_____

_____

What are the first aid steps to take when you see someone having an asthma attack? **Circle Yes** for each action you should take **or No** for each action you should not take.

(CALL 9-1-1) if the victim is not known to have asthma.   Yes   No

Help the victim use his or her prescribed inhaler as directed by his or her medical provider.   Yes   No

Have the victim breathe into a paper bag for a few minutes.   Yes   No

Give the victim an aspirin as quickly as possible.   Yes   No

Have the victim lie on his or her back with his or her feet raised.   Yes   No

Breathing Difficulty

Many different illnesses or injuries may cause breathing difficulty.

FIRST AID STEPS

1. (CALL 9-1-1) immediately for sudden unexplained breathing problems.
2. Help the victim rest in a position of easiest breathing. Calm and reassure the victim.
3. Hyperventilation is fast, deep breathing caused by stress or anxiety. If the victim is hyperventilating, ask him or her to breathe slowly.
4. Ask the victim about any prescribed medication he or she may have and help the victim take it if needed.
5. Stay with the victim and be prepared to give CPR if breathing stops.

Hypoglycemia and Diabetic Emergencies

 Video Review

Differentiate between the signs and symptoms of low blood sugar and high blood sugar.

_____

_____

Complete the following statements:

Give _____ to a victim experiencing low blood sugar.*

Call _____ if the victim becomes unresponsive or continues to have significant signs and symptoms.

* If you do not know whether a diabetic person is experiencing low or high blood sugar, still give sugar. It will not further harm a victim experiencing high blood sugar, but it may save the life of a diabetic experiencing low blood sugar.

A diabetic emergency may occur if the body's balance of insulin and blood sugar is disrupted.

Remember to:
- Ask the person if he or she is diabetic.
- Look for a medical alert ID.
- Give the victim glucose tablets if available. If **not** available, give another sugar source, such as candy or orange juice.
- **Only** give the victim sugar if he or she can follow simple commands and is able to swallow.
- (CALL 9-1-1) if the victim becomes unresponsive or continues to have significant signs and symptoms.

Fainting

When should you (CALL 9-1-1) if a person faints?

_____

Presyncope

Video Review

What are the common causes of presyncope?

_____

_____

First Aid for Sudden Dizziness or Near Fainting (Presyncope)

SIGNS AND SYMPTOMS

Sudden dizziness or near fainting can occur for number of reasons, including rising from a seated or lying position too quickly, dehydration, or other medical conditions. Oftentimes, the feeling of dizziness is accompanied by signs and symptoms including:

- Pale or ashen skin
- Sweating
- Weakness
- Changes in vision

FIRST AID STEPS

1. If a victim feels dizzy or lightheaded, or as if they are going to faint, and you **do not** suspect they are having a heart attack or stroke, take the following actions:
2. Assist the victim into a sitting or lying down position.
3. Instruct the victim to perform counterpressure maneuvers. Counterpressure maneuvers are actions a victim can take to help improve circulation to the heart and brain. They include:
   a. If sitting, have the victim lean forward with their head between their knees.
   b. If lying down, have the victim cross one leg over the other and ask them to squeeze or tense the muscles in their legs, abdomen, and buttocks.
4. Have the victim perform the counterpressure maneuvers until their symptoms go away.
5. If symptoms are **not** relieved in 1-2 minutes, or if the victim becomes unresponsive, (CALL 9-1-1) and get an AED. Check the victim's breathing and be ready to start CPR if needed.
6. If the victim is showing signs of a possible heart attack or stroke, **do not** perform counterpressure maneuvers. (CALL 9-1-1), give first aid for heart attack or stroke, and be ready to start CPR if needed.

Abdominal Pain

When should you seek medical attention for an adult with abdominal pain?

_____

_____

_____

_____

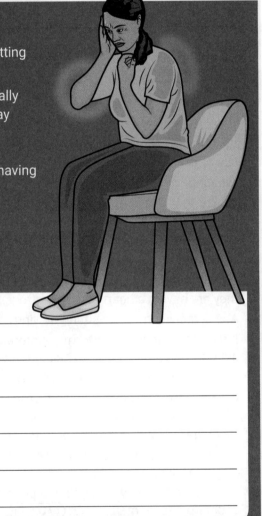

Scenario 1: Aunt Ursula

First, read the scenario. Then, talk with another participant sitting beside you about what you would do.

Aunt Ursula is visiting your family for a few days. She generally seems to be in good health. About an hour after a big holiday meal, she says she does not feel well. She has been feeling pressure in her chest since she ate, and she is sweating. Remembering your first aid course, you think she might be having a heart attack, but she says she thinks it is only indigestion caused by all that food. "I do not want to cause trouble for anyone," she says. "I will just sit here until it goes away."

What do you say to her? If she keeps insisting that it's only indigestion, what can you do?

_____

_____

_____

_____

_____

Scenario 2: An Office Worker's Seizure

As you are walking past the office of Sam, a coworker, you hear an odd thump and look in to see that Sam has fallen to the floor and is having a seizure. You remember that Sam once told you he has been treated for epilepsy. You rush into the office to help.

How can you help Sam during the seizure?

_____

How can you help Sam after the seizure?

_____

In what situation should you (CALL 9-1-1) for Sam?

_____

 Always call 9-1-1 for a seizure victim if the person is not known to have epilepsy.

Module Summary: First Aid for Sudden Illness and Heart Attack

- Feeling ill, dizzy, confused or weak
- Skin color changes (flushed, pale or ashen)
- Sweating
- Nausea, vomiting

Sudden Illness

FIRST AID STEPS

1. (CALL 9-1-1) for any unexplained sudden illness.
2. Help the victim rest.
3. Prevent the victim from becoming chilled or overheated.
4. Reassure the victim.
5. **Do not** give the victim anything to eat or drink.
6. Watch for changes and be prepared to give CPR if needed.

Heart Attack

FIRST AID STEPS

1. (CALL 9-1-1) for any victim experiencing chest discomfort, even if the victim says it is not serious.
2. Help the victim rest in a comfortable position. Loosen constricting clothing.
3. Ask the victim if he or she is taking heart medication, and help obtain the medication. Follow the directions on the medication.
4. Encourage the victim to chew and swallow 1 adult aspirin (325 mg) or 2-4 low-dose "baby" aspirin (81 mg each) unless he or she is allergic to aspirin or **cannot** take aspirin for any other reason.
5. Stay with the victim and be reassuring and calming.
6. Be ready to give CPR if needed.
7. **Do not** let the victim eat or drink anything (including water).

Module Summary:
First Aid for Hypoglycemia and Diabetic Emergencies

FIRST AID STEPS

1. Ask the person if he or she is diabetic or prone to becoming hypoglycemic.

2. Look for a medical alert ID.

3. Give the victim glucose tablets, if available. If **not** available, give another sugar source, such as candy, orange juice, or a glucose gel. If a child is **not** willing or able to swallow glucose, a mixture of granulated sugar and water can be applied under the tongue.

4. **Only** give the victim sugar if he or she is awake and can follow simple commands and is able to swallow.

5. (CALL 9-1-1) if the victim becomes unresponsive, symptoms worsen, or their symptoms **do not** improve within 10 minutes.

First Aid for Presyncope (Dizziness/Near Fainting)

SIGNS AND SYMPTOMS

O Pale or ashen skin

O Sweating

O Weakness

O Changes in vision

FIRST AID STEPS

1. Assist the victim into a sitting or lying down position.

2. Instruct the victim to perform counterpressure maneuvers. Counterpressure maneuvers are actions a victim can take to help improve circulation to the heart and brain. They include:

    a. If sitting, have the victim lean forward with their head between their knees.

    b. If lying down, have the victim cross one leg over the other and ask them to squeeze or tense the muscles in their legs, abdomen, and buttocks.

3. Have the victim perform the counterpressure maneuvers until their symptoms go away.

4. If symptoms are **not** relieved in 1-2 minutes, or if the victim becomes unresponsive, (CALL 9-1-1) and get an AED. Check the victim's breathing and be ready to start CPR if needed.

🔔 If the victim is showing signs of a possible heart attack or stroke, do not perform counterpressure maneuvers. Call 9-1-1, give first aid for heart attack or stroke, and be ready to start CPR if needed.

Poisoning and Allergic Reactions

Objectives

- Decide when to call the **Poison Control Center** or (CALL 9-1-1) in cases of poisoning.
- Identify first aid steps for victims of swallowed poison.
- Identify first aid steps for victims of inhaled poison.
- In industrial settings, state the importance of gathering information on the location and effects of chemicals, the Safety Data Sheets (SDSs) and other chemical emergency information, and the location of antidote supplies.
- Identify the steps of first aid for a victim with:
  - A snake bite
  - A spider bite
  - A bee or wasp sting
  - A scorpion sting
  - A tick bite
- Determine the first aid for a victim of Poison Ivy, Oak or Sumac.
- List the causes of a severe allergic reaction.
- Describe first aid for a severe allergic reaction.
- Describe first aid for opioid drug overdose.
- Demonstrate how to use an auto-injector to administer a life-saving medication.
- Describe how to administer naloxone via nasal spray to stop an opioid overdose.

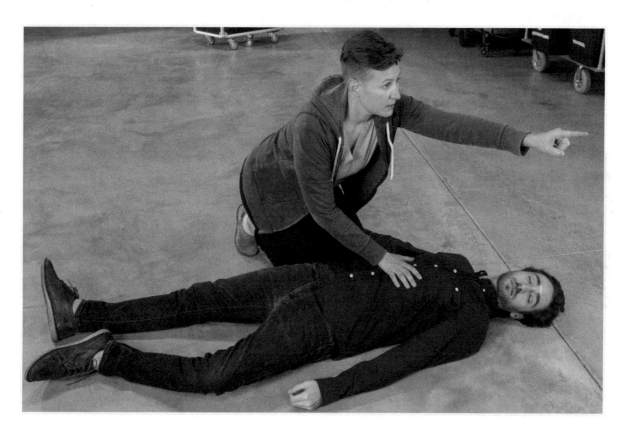

Poisoning – Inhaled or Swallowed

Video Review

Circle True or False for each of the following statements:

Call the Poison Control Center only if you know the exact ingredients in the poison that might have been involved.	True	False
Never induce vomiting for a poisoning victim.	True	False
Carbon monoxide poisoning from a faulty home furnace may cause headache, nausea and changing levels of responsiveness.	True	False
Accidentally taking too much of a prescribed or over-the-counter medication may cause a poisoning emergency.	True	False

Workplace Toxins

If you work with chemicals or toxic substances in your workplace, ensure you are informed of:

- The location and effects of chemicals
- The location of Safety Data Sheets (SDSs) and other chemical emergency information
- The location of antidote supplies

Bites and Stings

Snake Bite

- The most common venomous snakes in the United States are the rattlesnake, copperhead, water moccasin (cottonmouth) and coral snake. Outside the United States, common venomous snakes include the Indian or spectacled cobra (South Asia) and the yellow eyelash pit viper (South America).
- (CALL 9-1-1) for any poisonous bite.

Rattlesnake

Copperhead

Spider Bite

- The most common venomous spiders in the United States are the black widow and the brown recluse spiders.
- (CALL 9-1-1) for any poisonous bite.

Black Widow

Bee or Wasp Sting, Scorpion Sting and Allergic Reaction (Severe)

- Some scorpions are venomous.
- Remember that bee and wasp stings may cause an allergic reaction. (CALL 9-1-1) if symptoms occur.

Scorpion

Tick Bite

Remove a tick by pulling gently.

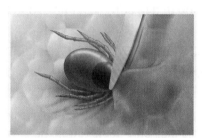

Tick bites can cause Lyme Disease

Severe Allergic Reactions

 Video Review

Circle True or False for the following statement:

Once a person with a serious allergic reaction has used an epinephrine auto-injector, you no longer need to (CALL 9-1-1).

True   False

Complete the following statement:

A person with serious allergies may be carrying _____.

A severe allergic reaction is also known as anaphylactic shock.

Possible causes include:

Notes:

- Certain drugs, such as penicillin
- Certain foods, such as peanuts and shellfish
- Certain substances, such as latex
- Insect stings and bites

SIGNS AND SYMPTOMS

- Difficulty breathing, wheezing, tightness in throat or chest
- Swelling of the face and neck, puffy eyes
- Anxiety or agitation
- Nausea, vomiting
- Changing levels of responsiveness

Using an Auto-Injector

Video Review

Circle True or False for each of the following statements:

In some situations, such as allergic reaction or overdose, it may be necessary to administer a second dose of medication if symptoms persist and arrival of EMS personnel may be delayed.
    True   **False**

For a drug overdose, it is not necessary to (CALL 9-1-1) if the person becomes responsive.
    True   **False**

An auto-injector may be used in some situations, to administer life-saving medication. Two common uses are to administer emergency epinephrine to a victim with a severe allergic reaction and to administer naloxone to a victim of an opioid drug overdose.

Administering Emergency Medication Using an Auto-Injector

Learn the Skill

Pair up with a classmate to practice administering emergency medication using an auto-injector. Practice this skill only using a training simulator — never with an actual auto-injector containing a needle and medication.

Remember that using the auto-injector is only part of the first aid for a victim with severe allergic reaction or an opioid drug overdose.

Performance Checklist

Skill Steps

☐ **1.** Take the auto-injector out of its case and remove the safety cap or protective cover.

☐ **2.** To administer the medication, press the auto-injector firmly against the victim's outer thigh. You will feel a "click" once the injection starts. Follow the manufacturer's instructions regarding how long to hold the device in place to ensure all of the medication has been delivered.

☐ **3.** Monitor the victim's breathing and be ready to give CPR if needed.

☐ **4.** If symptoms continue and EMS personnel have **not** yet arrived, administer a second dose using a second auto-injector, following the manufacturer's instructions.

☐ **5.** Help a responsive victim sit up in a position of easiest breathing. Put an unresponsive victim who is breathing in the recovery position.

☐ **Complete Skill**

Opioid Drug Overdose

Opioid drugs include heroin, morphine, oxycodone (Oxycontin), methadone, hydrocodone (Vicodin), codeine and some other prescription pain medications.

SIGNS AND SYMPTOMS

Pinpoint pupils, unresponsiveness, slow shallow breathing; in severe cases, victim's lips and nail beds may turn bluish or ashen, seizures may occur.

A drug called naloxone is a special lifesaving medication that can be used to stop an opioid overdose. Naloxone is most commonly administered through a nasal spray, or through an auto-injector. The auto-injector used for an opioid drug overdose is similar to the auto-injector used for a severe allergic reaction.

Always follow the instructions on the kit's labeling, and (CALL 9-1-1) even if the person becomes responsive.

FIRST AID STEPS

If a person is unresponsive and not breathing normally, and you suspect that the person has had an opioid overdose:

1. (CALL 9-1-1)
2. Get an AED and naloxone if they are available.
3. Start CPR and use the AED.
4. Administer the naloxone as soon as you can, but **do not** delay CPR to give naloxone.

Administering Naloxone via Nasal Spray

To administer naloxone using a nasal spray, follow these instructions:

1. Remove the nasal spray device from its packaging and follow the manufacturer's instructions for use. Some nasal spray devices may require need to be assembled before use.
2. Place the nozzle of the device firmly in either nostril.
3. Press the plunger firmly to administer all of the medication into the nose. Be sure to administer the entire dose.
4. If the victim is still unresponsive and **not** breathing, continue CPR and use an AED when available.
5. If the victim **does not** improve in 2-3 minutes, give an additional dose of naloxone if available.

While you should give naloxone as soon as possible, **do not** delay CPR to give naloxone.

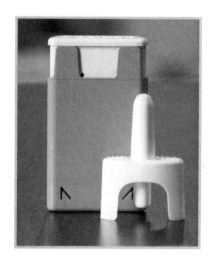

Administering Naloxone via Nasal Spray

Learn the Skill

To administer naloxone using a nasal spray, follow these instructions:

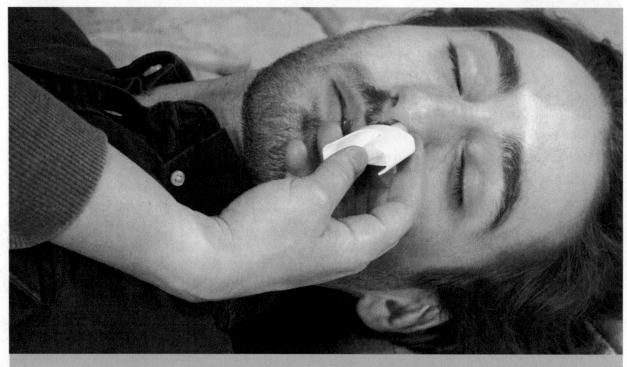

Performance Checklist

Skill Steps

- [ ] 1. Remove the nasal spray device from its packaging and follow the manufacturer's instructions for use. Some nasal spray devices may require need to be assembled before use.

- [ ] 2. Place the nozzle of the device firmly in either nostril.

- [ ] 3. Press the plunger firmly to administer all of the medication into the nose. Be sure to administer the entire dose.

- [ ] 4. If the victim is still unresponsive and **not** breathing, continue CPR and use an AED when available.

- [ ] 5. If the victim **does not** improve in 2-3 minutes, give an additional dose of naloxone if available.

 While you should give naloxone as soon as possible, **do not** delay CPR to give naloxone.

- [ ] **Complete Skill**

Poison Ivy, Oak, Sumac

What are the first aid steps to take if you come in contact with one of these plants?

_____

_____

_____

_____

_____

_____

_____

_____

Notes:

Poison Ivy

Poison Oak

Poison Sumac

Scenario 1: Uncle Joe

You arrive home late in the afternoon and find Uncle Joe, who is elderly and has health problems, unresponsive on the kitchen floor. You quickly check and determine that he is breathing. You carefully position him in the recovery position, and as you cross the room to the telephone, you notice several pill bottles on the table. One is open, and a number of capsules have spilled out on the table. You believe Uncle Joe might be experiencing an overdose poisoning.

On the wall beside the telephone is the number for the **Poison Control Center**: **(800) 222-1222**. Should you call the Poison Control Center or (CALL 9-1-1)? Why?

_____

Why did you put him in the recovery position?

_____

What do you do while waiting for help to arrive?

_____

Scenario 2: At the Restaurant

You are eating out at an Asian restaurant with friends when you notice that a man alone at the next table suddenly seems quite ill. He is wheezing and apparently having difficulty breathing, and his face looks swollen. You ask him if he is OK, and his agitated reply is that he thinks he ate something "bad for me." You ask if he has any food allergies, and he mumbles, "Peanuts." He fumbles in his pocket and produces what you recognize as an epinephrine auto-injector, but he is confused and drops it on the floor. His skin has become flushed, and his breathing is becoming more difficult.

What is the first action you should take?

_____

You pick up the auto-injector and quickly check the instructions on the label. You ask him if he can use it, but he just stares at you. What should you do now?

_____

What else can you now do to help him while waiting for emergency responders to arrive?

_____

Module Summary:
First Aid for Swallowed Poisons  (IMMEDIATE HELP IS NEEDED!)

FIRST AID STEPS

1. Determine what was swallowed, when and how much.

2. For a responsive victim, call the **Poison Control Center (800) 222-1222** immediately and follow its instructions.

3. For a victim with signs of a life-threatening condition (including sleepiness, seizures, difficulty breathing, vomiting) and for any unresponsive victim, (CALL 9-1-1).

4. Put an unresponsive breathing victim in the recovery position. Be prepared for vomiting. Monitor the victim's breathing and be ready to give CPR if needed.

5. **Do not** give the victim any substance to eat or drink unless instructed by the Poison Control Center. **Do not** follow first aid instructions present on some household product labels; instead follow the Poison Control Center's instructions.

First Aid for Inhaled Poisons  (IMMEDIATE HELP IS NEEDED!)

FIRST AID STEPS

1. Immediately move the victim into fresh air.

2. (CALL 9-1-1) even if the victim starts to recover.

3. Monitor the victim's breathing and be ready to give CPR if needed.

4. Put an unresponsive, breathing victim in the recovery position.

5. Loosen tight clothing around the neck or chest.

First Aid for Severe Allergic Reaction

FIRST AID STEPS

1. (CALL 9-1-1)

2. Help a responsive victim use his or her emergency epinephrine auto-injector. If the victim **cannot** use the prescribed auto-injector, you may administer it yourself if permitted by state law.

3. Follow the manufacturer's instructions for using the auto-injector and administering a second dose if EMS personnel are **not** expected to arrive within 5-10 minutes.

4. Monitor the victim's breathing and be ready to give CPR if needed.

5. Help a responsive victim sit up in a position of easiest breathing. Put an unresponsive victim who is breathing in the recovery position.

12 Cold and Heat Emergencies

Objectives

- Describe the signs of a cold emergency.
- Describe the signs of a heat emergency.
- Identify the first aid for:
  - Frostbite
  - Hypothermia
  - Heat cramps
  - Exertional dehydration
  - Heat exhaustion
  - Heat stroke

Video Review

Which of the following are signs and symptoms of severe hypothermia?
Check all that apply.

☐ Victim feels feverish   ☐ Frequent need to urinate

☐ Victim seems clumsy or drowsy   ☐ Altered breathing

☐ State of lethargy or confusion   ☐ Changing levels of responsiveness

☐ Skin is very red

Complete the following statements:

For a victim with severe hypothermia, check for _____ and

_____ , and call _____ .

Warm a victim with hypothermia using _____ or

_____ .

For a heat stroke victim, list 3 ways to cool the person's body as quickly as possible:

1. _____

2. _____

3. _____

Cold and Heat Emergencies

Hypothermia and heat stroke are life-threatening emergencies. Frostbite and heat exhaustion are usually less serious.

Prevent heat and cold injuries by dressing appropriately and avoiding prolonged exposure to temperature extremes. Stay well hydrated and rested.

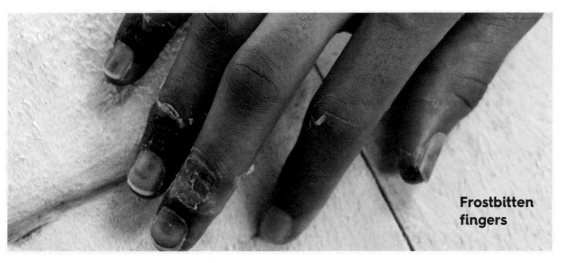

Frostbitten fingers

Frostbite and Hypothermia

In what circumstances should you actively rewarm frostbitten fingers or toes by immersing them in lukewarm water?

_____

_____

_____

_____

_____

_____

_____

_____

_____

_____

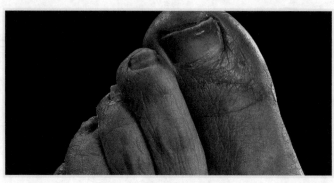
Frostbitten toes

Frostbitten hand

Circle True or **False** for the following statement:

If a victim found in the cold is not shivering, then he or she cannot have hypothermia.

True   False

Heat Exhaustion, Heat Stroke and Exertional Dehydration

Heat exhaustion will develop into heat stroke if the victim is not cooled and given water. But someone who has engaged in strenuous activity in the heat may develop exertional heat stroke without first having shown signs of heat exhaustion.

Heat exhaustion

Heat stroke

Scenario 1: The Company Picnic

Your company's annual picnic and softball game happens to fall on the hottest day of the year. By the seventh inning, your team's center fielder seems to be showing signs and symptoms of heat exhaustion.

Name 2 signs or symptoms that strongly suggest heat exhaustion.

1. _____

2. _____

What are the first aid steps to help the victim?

_____

_____

_____

_____

_____

_____

Module Summary: First Aid for Cold and Heat Emergencies

Frostbite

`FIRST AID STEPS`

1. Move the victim out of the cold and into a warm place.
2. Remove wet clothing and constricting items.
3. Protect between fingers and toes with dry gauze.
4. Seek medical attention as soon as possible.
5. Warm frostbitten area in lukewarm water (99-104°F or 37-40°C) for 20-30 minutes **only** if medical care will be delayed and there is **no** danger of the skin refreezing. **Do not** use chemical warmers directly on frostbitten tissue.
6. Protect and elevate the area.

Hypothermia

`FIRST AID STEPS`

1. Check responsiveness and breathing and `CALL 9-1-1`. Except in mild cases, the victim needs immediate medical care.
2. Provide CPR if unresponsive and **not** breathing normally.
3. Quickly move the victim out of the cold. Remove any wet clothing.
4. Warm the victim with blankets or warm clothing.
5. Only if the victim is far from medical care, use active rewarming by putting the victim near a heat source and putting warm (but **not** hot) water in containers against the skin.
6. **Do not** rub or massage the victim's skin.
7. Be very gentle when handling the victim.
8. Give warm (**not** hot) drinks to an alert victim who can easily swallow, but **do not** give alcohol or caffeine.
9. Monitor breathing and be ready to give CPR if needed.

Heat Exhaustion

`FIRST AID STEPS`

1. Move the victim out of the heat to rest in a cool place, and loosen or remove outer clothing.
2. Cool the victim with a cool water spray or wet cloths on the forehead and body.
3. Give the victim a carbohydrate-electrolyte drink, such as a sports drink, to promote rehydration. (Other beverages, such as 2% milk and coconut water are also effective.) If a carbohydrate-electrolyte drink is **not** available, give the victim water.

Heat Stroke

`FIRST AID STEPS`

1. `CALL 9-1-1`
2. Move the victim to a cool place.
3. Remove outer clothing.
4. Immediately cool the victim with any means at hand, preferably by immersing the victim up to the neck in cold water (with the help of a second rescuer). If immersion in cold water is **not** possible, place the victim in a cold shower, **or** move to a cool area and cover as much of the body as possible with cold, wet towels.
5. **Do not** try to force the victim to drink liquids.
6. Monitor the victim's breathing and be ready to give CPR if needed.

Rescuing and Moving Victims

Objectives

- Describe what to do when a victim needs to be rescued from a dangerous situation.
- Describe what to do when multiple victims need first aid.
- Identify situations in which it is acceptable to move a victim.
- Describe how to move a victim when necessary.

Video Review

When should you move an injured victim?

_____

_____

_____

_____

Complete the following statements.

Moving a victim can increase the risk of further injury, so support the victim's

_____ and _____ as much as possible.

If there are hazards at the scene, _____ and leave the rescue
to the professionals.

Victim Rescue

- **Never** put yourself at risk to rescue a victim.
- **Never** enter an unsafe situation if hazards are present. (CALL 9-1-1) and leave the rescue
  to the professionals.
- **Do not** try to perform any rescue technique you have not been trained to do.

Notes:

Caring for Multiple Victims

Quickly check all victims and give care first to the highest-priority victims who cannot wait for help.

Priorities for Multiple Victims			
Priority	Victim's Condition	Severity	Examples
First	Critical	Victims with life-threatening injuries who cannot wait for help	• Airway or breathing problems • Severe bleeding • Shock • Severe burns
Second	Serious	Victims with injuries who need care very soon but may be able to wait for help	• Burns • Broken bones • Other injuries without severe bleeding
Third	Stable	Victims who can wait for some time	• Minor injuries • Victims who can walk
Fourth	Obviously dead or dying	Victims who cannot be saved	• No signs of breathing and signs of severe bleeding (unless there are no first-priority victims)

Moving Victims Safely

Move an injured victim only if:

• You are with the victim in a dangerous environment, such as:
  ▪ Fire or explosion is likely.
  ▪ Poisonous fumes are present.
  ▪ The structure is collapsing.
• The victim needs to be moved into position for lifesaving care, such as CPR.
• The victim is in the way of another seriously injured victim.

If you determine to move a victim, remember:

• Moving a victim is liable to cause further injury.
• If you are **not** physically able to move the victim yourself, get help from others.
• Support the head and neck as much as possible.

Techniques for Moving Victims

Below are several techniques for moving victims based on the situation.

2-rescuer assist

Piggyback carry

Shoulder drag

Cradle carry

Clothes drag

Module Summary: First Aid for Rescuing and Moving Victims

FIRST AID STEPS

1. **Never** risk your own safety in an attempt to rescue a victim from a dangerous situation.

2. **Never** enter a scene where hazards are present. (CALL 9-1-1) and leave the rescue to the professionals.

3. With multiple victims, first treat those with life-threatening injuries who **cannot** wait for help but who can be saved.

4. Consider moving an injured victim **only** if:

   a. You are already with the victim in a dangerous environment (such as a risk of fire or explosion, poisonous fumes, structural collapse).

   b. The victim needs to be moved into position for lifesaving care, such as CPR.

   c. The victim is in the way of a more seriously injured victim.

14 CPR and AED

Objectives

- Recognize when cardiopulmonary resuscitation (CPR) and use of an automated external defibrillator (AED) are needed.
- Identify the links in the cardiac chain of survival.
- State when CPR is needed.
- Identify when and how rescue breaths are given along with chest compressions.
- Explain the importance of using a barrier device for rescue breaths.
- State when CPR can stop.
- Identify when and how Hands-Only CPR (compression-only) can be given.
- Demonstrate how to correctly perform the head tilt-chin lift.
- Demonstrate how to give CPR to an adult, child and infant using the correct rate and
- depth of chest compressions.
- Identify when and how to use an AED.
- Demonstrate how to use an AED on an adult, child and infant.

The Cardiac Chain of Survival

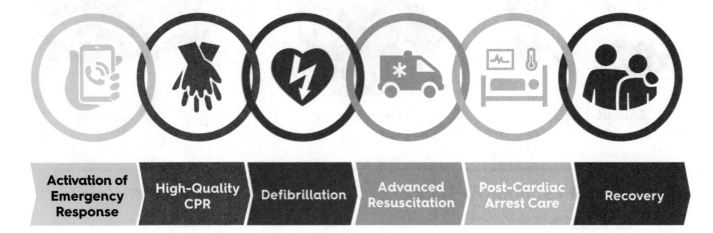

| Activation of Emergency Response | High-Quality CPR | Defibrillation | Advanced Resuscitation | Post-Cardiac Arrest Care | Recovery |

1. **Recognition and activation of the emergency response system** — identify the emergency and call for help (CALL 9-1-1) or local emergency number).

2. **Immediate high-quality CPR** — call for an AED and start CPR immediately.

3. **Rapid defibrillation** — use the AED as soon as it is available.

4. **Advanced Resuscitation** — the sooner the victim receives professional care, the better the chance for survival.

5. **Post-arrest care** — the victim needs continued medical care.

6. **Recovery** — the victim will need time and support for their recovery.

CPR

CPR Skill Steps

☐ **1.** For an unresponsive victim who is not breathing or only gasps occasionally, send someone to (CALL 9-1-1) (or your local emergency number) and get an AED. If alone with an adult, first (CALL 9-1-1) and get an AED if available nearby. If alone with a child, first give 2 minutes of CPR and then (CALL 9-1-1) and get an AED if available.

☐ **2.** Expose the chest. Place hands in correct position for chest compressions.
    a. For adults: in center of chest, with one hand on top of the other.
    b. For children: in center of chest with one or two hands.
    c. For infants: two fingers or 2 thumbs just below the nipple line. (The heel of one hand may be considered if the rescuer **cannot** compress to the recommended depth using fingers or thumbs).

    Do not give compressions over the bottom tip of the breastbone. For an adult or child, keep fingers off the chest and do not lean on the chest. Keep your elbows straight and keep your hands in contact with the chest at all times.

☐ **3.** Give 30 chest compressions at a rate of 100-120 per minute. Count aloud for a steady fast rate: "1, 2, 3 . . ."
    a. For adults: to a depth of at least 2 inches but not more than 2.4 inches.
    b. For children (age 1 to puberty): to a depth of $\frac{1}{3}$ the depth of the chest, or about 2 inches.
    c. For infants (to age 1): to a depth of $\frac{1}{3}$ the depth of the chest, or about $1\frac{1}{2}$ inches.

    Do not lean on the chest in between compressions; let the chest rise completely after each compression.

☐ **4.** Tilt the head and lift the chin to open the airway. Give 2 rescue breaths, each lasting 1 second. (If the first breath **does not** go in, reposition the head and try again; if the second breath still **does not** go in, look in the mouth and remove any object seen.)

    🔔 *If you are unable or unwilling to provide rescue breaths to an unresponsive victim who is not breathing, perform Hands-Only CPR (also known as compression-only CPR) by compressing the chest hard and fast (100-120 per minute). Note that conventional CPR is preferred for pediatric victims.*

☐ **5.** Continue cycles of 30 compressions and 2 breaths.

☐ **6.** Continue CPR until:
    • Victim wakes up.
    • An AED is brought to the scene and is ready to use.
    • Professional help arrives and takes over.
    • If the victim starts breathing normally but is unresponsive, put the victim in the recovery position and monitor breathing.

☐ **7.** When an AED arrives, start the AED sequence.

☐ **Complete Skill**

CPR with Opioid-Associated Life-Threatening Emergency

If the victim is unresponsive and not breathing normally as a result of a possible opioid drug overdose, the life-saving medication naloxone should be administered in addition to CPR, if it is available. See Module 11 – Poisoning and Allergic Reactions for more information on administering naloxone. The following are steps for CPR and AED in opioid drug overdose:

FIRST AID STEPS

1. For an unresponsive victim who is **not** breathing or only gasps occasionally, send someone to (CALL 9-1-1) (or your local emergency number) and get an AED and naloxone. If alone with the victim, first give 2 minutes of CPR and then (CALL 9-1-1) and get naloxone and an AED if available.

2. Administer naloxone as soon as available, but **do not** delay CPR. Naloxone may be repeated after 2-3 minutes if the victim's condition **does not** improve. (Refer to Module 11 – Poisoning and Allergic Reactions for information on naloxone administration.

3. If the victim **does not** respond or begin breathing regularly, continue CPR and use the AED as soon as available.

4. Continue to check responsiveness and for normal breathing until EMS personnel arrive. If the victim responds or begins breathing regularly, continue to monitor and be prepared to resume CPR and repeat naloxone if the victim stops responding.

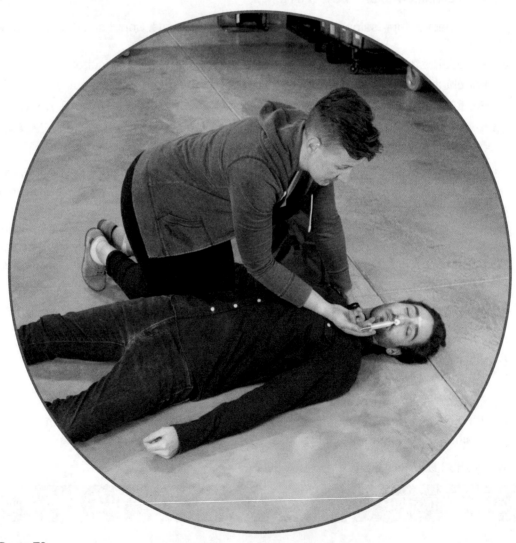

AED
Performance Checklist

Skill Steps

☐ 1. Position victim away from water and metal. Place unit by victim's shoulder and turn it on.

☐ 2. Expose victim's chest and quickly dry or shave the pad placement areas if necessary.

☐ 3. Apply pads to victim's chest as shown on pads. If needed, plug cables into unit.
Use adult pads for a victim age 8 or older. For an infant or child younger than 8, use pediatric pads if available, applied as directed by the unit; if pediatric pads are unavailable, use adult pads.

☐ 4. Stand clear during rhythm analysis.

☐ 5. Follow prompts from AED unit to take one of three actions:
    a. Press the Shock button,
    b. Stay clear while the AED automatically delivers a shock, or
    c. **Do not** shock but immediately give CPR with the pads remaining in place, starting with chest compressions.

☐ 6. Follow the AED's prompts to analyze the rhythm again after 5 cycles of CPR (about 2 minutes).

☐ 7. Continue steps 5 and 6 until the victim wakes up or professional rescuers arrive and take over.

☐ 8. If the victim starts breathing normally but is unresponsive, put the victim in the recovery position (with pads remaining in place) and continue to monitor breathing.

☐ **Complete Skill**

CPR and AED for Infants, Children and Adults

	Infant Under a 1 year	**Child** 1 year to Puberty, except 1–8 for AED.	**Adult**
Check for responsiveness and normal breathing	• Stimulate to check response. • Observe whether breathing normally.	• Tap shoulder, and shout "Are you OK?" while checking for normal breathing (gasps are **not** normal)	• Tap shoulder, and shout "Are you OK?" while checking for normal breathing (gasps are **not** normal)
If unresponsive, have someone (CALL 9-1-1) **for help**	• Send someone to (CALL 9-1-1). If alone, give 2 minutes of care **before** calling 9-1-1 (and getting an AED).	• Send someone to (CALL 9-1-1). If alone, unless the child has a known heart problem, give 2 minutes of care **before** calling 9-1-1 (and getting an AED).	• Send someone to (CALL 9-1-1). If alone, (CALL 9-1-1), and get an AED immediately (give 2 minutes of care **first** for a drowning victim).
If unresponsive, and not breathing normally, give CPR, starting with chest compressions	• For compressions, use 2 fingers or 2 thumbs just below the nipple line. (The heel of one hand may be considered if the rescuer cannot compress to the recommended depth using fingers or thumbs).	• For compressions, use 1 or 2 hands midway between nipples. Compress chest to at least $1/3$ the depth of chest (about 2 inches).	• For compressions, use both hands midway betwee, one on top of the other, midway between nipples. Compress chest at least 2 inches but not more than 2.4 inches.
Chest compressions in CPR	• Chest compressions at a rate of 100-120 per minute	• Chest compressions at a rate of 100-120 per minute	• Chest compressions at a rate of 100-120 per minute
Ratio of compressions and breaths	• Cycles of 30 compressions and 2 breaths	• Cycles of 30 compressions and 2 breaths	• Cycles of 30 compressions and 2 breaths

Notes:

CPR and AED for Infants, Children and Adults

Quick Reference

	Infant Under a 1 year	**Child** 1 year to Puberty, except 1-8 for AED.	**Adult**
Give 2 breaths	• Use barrier device or cover mouth, nose or stoma. Each breath given over 1 second.	• Use barrier device or cover mouth, nose or stoma. Each breath given over 1 second.	• Use barrier device or cover mouth, nose or stoma. Each breath given over 1 second.
If breaths still do not go in, reposition head and try again	• Each breath given over 1 second	• Each breath given over 1 second	• Each breath given over 1 second
If breaths still do not go in, continue with chest compressions	• Continue with chest compressions. Check the mouth for an object each time breaths are given, and remove it if seen.	• Continue with chest compressions. Check the mouth for an object each time breaths are given, and remove it if seen.	• Continue with chest compressions. Check the mouth for an object each time breaths are given, and remove it if seen.
Use AED as soon as possible	• Use pediatric AED electrode pads if available. If **not**, use adult pads.	• Use pediatric AED electrode pads if available. If **not**, use adult pads.	• Use adult AED electrode pads.
If victim recovers normal breathing, put in recovery position	• Hold infant and monitor breathing.	• Lay on side in recover position and monitor breathing.	• Lay on side in recover position and monitor breathing.

Cardiac Arrest in Pregnancy

If you encounter a pregnant woman in cardiac arrest, **don't** delay starting CPR. High quality CPR can increase both the mother and the unborn child's chances for survival. Perform CPR on a pregnant woman the same way you would for any other adult victim. If the recovery position on her left side.

Rescuing the Rescuer

Often, rescuers may not be prepared for the feelings or emotions they experience after providing CPR or first aid care. Debriefings and referrals to professionals who are trained in critical incident stress can be beneficial for rescuers. Rescuers should participate in debriefings following a resuscitative effort and should consider consulting a professional for support.

Scenario 1: The Jogger

You are at the beach with a group of people when a man jogging by suddenly collapses and falls face down on the sand. Provide care from the moment you arrive at the victim's side, with all actions in the correct sequence. Follow your instructor's descriptions of how the victim responds.

Scenario 2: The Baseball Game

You are at a youth baseball game when a child at bat is struck in the chest by a pitch. He falls to the ground and does not move. Provide care with all actions in the correct sequence. Follow your instructor's descriptions of how the victim responds.

Fundamentals of CPR and AED

Fill in the correct answers:

For an adult whom you see collapse, start CPR as soon as you determine the victim is _____ and not _____ normally.

In each cycle of CPR, rapidly compress the chest _____ times and then give _____ breaths.

If the AED advises giving a shock, immediately after this shock, you should perform CPR starting with _____ for about _____ minutes and then follow the AED prompts.

Circle True or False for each of the following statements:

If you are alone with an adult you see collapse suddenly, you should (CALL 9-1-1) before starting to give CPR.   True   False

Give chest compressions at a rate of 1 every second.   True   False

It is OK to use pediatric AED pads on an adult.   True   False

When giving a breath during CPR, breathe into the victim for about 1 second.   True   False

When giving chest compressions, allow the chest to move all the way back up between compressions.   True   False

Begin CPR with 2 quick breaths before starting compressions.   True   False

Module Summary: Key Principles of CPR and AED

○ (CALL 9-1-1) **or your local emergency number for an unresponsive victim.**
  · For unresponsive victims who are **not** breathing normally, use the CPR technique that allows you to confidently deliver good-quality chest compressions with minimal interruption.

○ **For CPR:**
  · Begin with 30 chest compressions hard and fast in the center of the chest. Compress the chest at least 2 inches but **not** more than 2.4 inches for an adult, or at least ⅓ the depth of the chest in an infant (about 1½ inches) or child (about 2 inches), giving compressions at a rate of at least 100-120 per minute. **Do not** lean on the chest in between compressions; let the chest rise completely after each compression.
  · Open the airway with the head tilt-chin lift and give 2 breaths, each for about 1 second, watching the chest rise and fall. Use a barrier device to give breaths, if available.
  · Continue with cycles of 30 compressions and 2 breaths.

○ **For Hands-Only CPR (compression-only):**
  · Push hard and fast in the center of the chest.

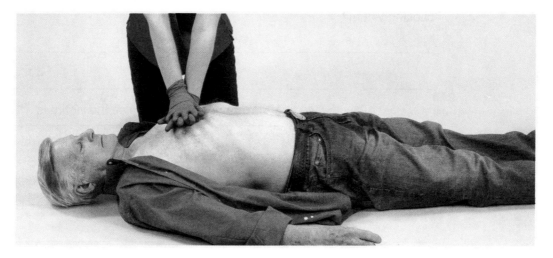

○ **Use the AED as soon as it is available and ready to use.**
  · Apply the pads to the victim's chest as shown on the pads. For an infant or child younger than 8, use pediatric pads if available.
  · Follow the AED prompts to give a shock when indicated, and then to continue CPR before the AED again analyzes the victim's rhythm.
  · If the victim begins breathing normally but remains unresponsive, position the victim in the recovery position and monitor breathing until help arrives.

Choking

Objectives

- Identify correct choking care for a responsive adult, child or infant with a partially obstructed airway who can cough.
- Describe how to give abdominal thrusts to a responsive, choking adult or child.
- Identify correct care for a choking victim who becomes unresponsive.
- Demonstrate how to provide choking care for a responsive adult or child.
- Demonstrate how to provide choking care for a responsive infant.

Video Review

If you believe a person is choking, what should you do?

_____

_____

_____

Where do you position your hands to give abdominal thrusts to a responsive choking victim?

_____

_____

_____

In what direction do you provide the abdominal thrusts?

_____

_____

_____

What is different about CPR given to an unresponsive choking victim, compared with conventional CPR for a victim not known to be choking?

_____

_____

_____

Choking Care for Responsive Adult or Child

Learn the Skill

Pair up with a classmate to practice choking care for a responsive victim.

Do not actually give abdominal thrusts to the other participant - this skill is to learn hand and body position.

Performance Checklist

Skill Steps

☐ 1. Stand behind the victim with 1 leg forward between the victim's legs. For a child, move down to the child's level. Keep your head slightly to one side.

☐ 2. Locate the person's navel with a finger from 1 hand.

☐ 3. Make a fist with the other hand and place the thumb side of the fist against the person's abdomen just above the navel.

☐ 4. Grasp your fist with your other hand and thrust inward and upward into the victim's abdomen with quick jerks. Continue abdominal thrusts until the victim expels the object or becomes unresponsive.

☐ 5. Instead of abdominal thrusts, give chest thrusts from behind the victim for:

- A responsive, pregnant victim
- Any victim you **cannot** get your arms around
- Any victim for whom abdominal thrusts are **not** effective
- Avoid squeezing the ribs with your arms.

☐ 6. If the victim becomes unresponsive (or for any suspected choking victim found unresponsive), lower the person to the ground, expose the chest, and start CPR with 30 chest compressions. Look inside the mouth each time you open the mouth to give breaths, and remove any object seen.

☐ Complete Skill

Notes:

Choking Care for Responsive Infant

Learn the Skill

Practice with an infant manikin.

 Give choking care only if the infant cannot cry, cough or breathe.

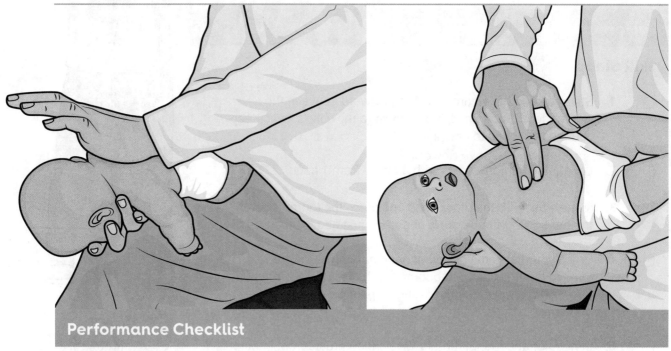

Performance Checklist

Skill Steps

☐ 1. Support the infant face down by holding the head in 1 hand, with the torso on your forearm against your thigh. Give up to 5 back blows (slaps) between the shoulder blades with the heel of your other hand.

☐ 2. If the object is **not** expelled, roll the infant face up, supporting the back of the head with your hand.

☐ 3. Place 2 fingers on the breastbone, just below the nipple line.

☐ 4. Give 5 chest thrusts, about 1 per second. Each thrust should be 1½ inches deep.

☐ 5. Continue cycles of 5 back blows (slaps) and 5 chest thrusts until the object is expelled or the infant becomes unresponsive. If alone, (CALL 9-1-1) after 2 minutes if **no one** has yet done so.

☐ 6. If the infant becomes unresponsive (or for any non-breathing, choking infant found unresponsive), give CPR. Look inside the mouth each time you open the mouth to give breaths and remove any object seen.

☐ **Complete Skill**

Module Summary: First Aid for Choking

O   If the person is coughing productively, encourage continued coughing to expel the obstructing item on his or her own.

O   If the person clutches his or her throat, looks frantic, or signals he or she is **not** getting enough air:
   1. Ask if the person is choking. If the victim nods or indicates yes, ask if you can help.
   2. Take position behind the victim, with your leg between his or her legs and your fist just above the navel.
   3. Give quick thrusts inward and upward to clear the object.

O   If a choking victim becomes unresponsive, give CPR, starting with chest compressions. Look inside the mouth each time you open the mouth to give breaths and remove any object seen.

Notes:

NSC First Aid, CPR & AED

Answer Sheet

Name _____   Date _____

1. a   b   c   d

2. a   b   c   d

3. a   b   c   d

4. a   b   c   d

5. a   b   c   d

6. a   b   c   d

7. a   b   c   d

8. a   b   c   d

9. a   b   c   d

10. a   b   c   d

11. a   b   c   d

12. a   b   c   d

13. a   b   c   d

14. a   b   c   d

15. a   b   c   d

16. a   b   c   d

17. a   b   c   d

18. a   b   c   d

19. a   b   c   d

20. a   b   c   d